Inside the Living Cell

Inside
the Living Cell

SOME SECRETS OF LIFE

J. A. V. BUTLER

D.SC., F.R.S.

New York

BASIC BOOKS, INC.

© George Allen and Unwin Ltd 1959

FOURTH PRINTING

LIBRARY OF CONGRESS CATALOG CARD NUMBER 59-8434
PRINTED IN THE UNITED STATES OF AMERICA

ACKNOWLEDGMENTS

I am greatly indebted to the following for providing the excellent photographs reproduced in this book: my colleagues, Messrs E. J. Ambrose, M. S. C. Birbeck, Drs O. G. Fahmy, E. H. Mercer and S. H. Revell and Professor P. Koller, of the Chester Beatty Research Institute; Dr J. C. Kendrew of the MRC Unit for Molecular Biology, Cambridge; Professor J. Z. Young, Dr H. E. Huxley and Dr D. Sholl of University College, London; Dr F. Sjöstrand of the Department of Anatomy, Karolinska Institute, Stockholm; Dr R. W. G. Wyckoff; and Professor F. Jacob of the Institut Pasteur, Paris. The following gave me permission to use line drawings: Dr Lorenté de No and the Oxford University Press; Dr W. F. Floyd of the Middlesex Hospital Medical School; Professor G. W. Beadle and Professor G. A. Baitsell and the University Presses of Oxford and Yale. I am indebted to The Pergamon Press for the loan of a block.

To all I tender my sincere thanks.

J.A.V.B.

PREFACE

'Wot I like in that 'ere style of writin',' said the elder Mr Weller, 'is that there ain't no callin' names in it.' There is plenty of 'callin' names' in this book and it is doubtful if Mr Weller would have approved of it. Many names are inevitable, even in a popular book about the nature of life, and the writer's chief problem is to know where to draw a line between what may be expected to be intelligible to general readers and technicalities. I have tried to make the style of this book reasonably simple while still maintaining a level of information and comment which, I hope, will not be without interest to students of science and also scientists who are not experts. No doubt readers will find some portions more difficult than others, but no harm will be done if they skip passages which they do not like.

It would be impossible to give authority for all the facts quoted without overburdening the text with references. Some indications as to where further information can be found are given in an Appendix, for those readers who would like to follow up particular subjects. The text is also supplemented by an Appendix containing a collection of chemical formulae of some of the compounds mentioned.

In writing this book I have made use, when appropriate, of passages from a previous book, *Man is a Microcosm,* which is now out of print. But the scope of the present book is much wider, quite apart from the fact that many parts of the subject have advanced radically in the last few years.

I am much indebted to Dr P. Rosbaud, who read the MS and made useful suggestions, and for his friendly assistance. I am also grateful to Miss Jill Emmerson, for coping with an untidy manuscript.

London
July 20, 1958

CONTENTS

PREFACE — 9

I Living Cells and What They Are Made Of — 15
II How the Cell Lives — 22
III Vitamins and Antivitamins — 28
IV Cell Division — 38
V Inside the Cell — 46
VI Genes and Mutations — 54
VII Effects of X-rays and Atomic Radiations on Living Cells — 58
VIII Viruses—Cell Parasites — 67
IX A Community of Cells — 75
X Chemical Messengers — 80
XI Antibodies and Immunity — 86
XII Cancer — 93
XIII The Origin of Life and Photosynthesis — 101
XIV Specialized Cells: Muscles, Nerves and Sense Organs — 110
XV The Brain and What It Does — 121
XVI Actions and How They Are Performed — 131
XVII Using Tools and Symbols — 137
XVIII Is the Brain a Calculating Machine? — 143
XIX Ageing and Death — 150
XX Life in the Universe — 156
APPENDIX I—*Chemical Formulae* — 163
APPENDIX II—*Selected References and Books for further Reading* — 167
INDEX — 171

ILLUSTRATIONS

1 A model of a protein molecule   16

2 An interference photograph of chromosomes in living cells   17

3 Chromosomes in the nucleus of cells from the growing tip of an onion root   32

4 The giant banded chromosomes of the salivary glands of the larva of the fly   33

5 A section of a rat liver taken with the electron microscope   48

6 A portion of a liver cell taken with the electron microscope at a higher magnification   49

7 Fine structure in the cell interior   64

8 Electron micrographs of Influenza A virus adhering to a red fowl cell   65

9 (a) The effect of a chemical substance (a nitrogen mustard) on the chromosomes of a tumour cell   80
   (b) The effect of X-rays on the chromosomes of a broad bean cell   80

10 (a) Turnip yellow virus   81
   (b) Two dissimilar bacterial cells (*B. coli*) in conjugation   81

11 Bacteriophage attacking a bacterium   96

12 A later stage of the attack of Bacteriophage   97

13 A cross-section of a chloroplast from *Aspidistra elatior*   112

14 Electron micrographs of muscle fibrils   113

15 A nerve cell of the mammalian spinal chord and the associated nerve fibre   128

16 Nerve cells in the visual cortex of the brain of a cat   129

and 28 *figures in text*

I

Living Cells and What They Are Made Of

꒳

Since all living things are either single cells or colonies of cells, the cell is the real unit of life and we shall have gone far in the understanding of life if we can find out what a single cell is made of and how it works. However, this is a colossal undertaking. Although it is tiny—the average cell is not more than 1/100 of a millimetre in diameter—we shall see that it contains a very large number of chemical substances, all connected by beautiful and complex mechanisms into a functioning whole. I shall try to explain something about these substances and about these mechanisms—in other words, about the life of the living cell.

We do not usually need to specify, at least for a bird's-eye view, what organism our cell belongs to. The remarkable fact has been established—and this is one of the most significant findings of the study of the chemistry of life—that all living organisms are very similarly constructed and operate in very similar ways. There are naturally quite large differences, e.g. between the cells of a woody plant, which contain much cellulose, and those of, say, a jellyfish in which the cells are entirely made of a jelly-like substance called protoplasm; but it is found that the basic organization of all cells has much in common. They are constructed to a considerable extent out of similar materials and the chemical operations which occur in them are basically the same. In other words all living things, from amoeba to man, are one family. The smallest body which exhibits all the properties of living things is the cell and it is only by studying life at the level of cells and their contents that we can hope to understand the secrets of living processes.

First of all, then, we must know something of what cells are made of. This study only really began in this century because it was impossible to describe adequately the characteristic substances present in cells until chemistry had advanced sufficiently to cope with them. In fact, only during the last twenty or thirty years has much progress been made in this study.

It has been known for a long time that living things are made of the same elementary substances as we are familiar with in ordinary life— carbon, oxygen, hydrogen, nitrogen and phosphorus and calcium are the commonest elements, but there are smaller quantities of many others.

A great profusion of 'organic' substances, like oils, fats, waxes, starch, resins, alcohols, sugars, had been obtained from living things. They were termed 'organic' to distinguish them from the 'inorganic' substances found in the earth, such as salt, ores, rocks, etc. An exact chemistry of 'organic' substances is a fairly recent development of science, going back only about one hundred years. Before that time, they were thought to be an entirely different type of material from 'inorganic' substances. But the distinction broke down when a German chemist, Wöhler, prepared in his laboratory from purely 'inorganic' materials (ammonia and carbon dioxide) the substance urea, which had previously been regarded as a typical product of life. Since then chemists have been able to synthesize in their laboratories an enormous number of 'organic' substances, including not only many which occur in nature, but also many thousands of others for which no natural counterpart exists. They were guided in this work by a knowledge of the rules of combination of atoms which were established by Van't Hoff and Kekulé. On the basis of these rules, it is possible to derive a formula for a compound which shows how its atoms are joined together. The formula is usually established by studying the reactions of the compound and by breaking it down into its component parts. It can be confirmed by building up a compound as represented by the formulae, to see if it corresponds with the original compound.

It soon appeared that it would be only a matter of time before all the compounds present in living cells could be synthesized in this way. However, it was eventually found that the more characteristic compounds of living cells, such as proteins, had a much greater complexity for which chemists were hardly prepared.

It had been recognized early in the nineteenth century that the most characteristic of the substances of living things were a type of nitrogenous compound called 'proteins'. These are familiar to everyone. They constitute a large part of animal tissues, e.g. they are the principal constituent of muscle, skin, nails, hair, the red cells of blood and the soluble substances present in blood serum, the casein of milk.

Every form of life—even plants, corals, jellyfish and bacteria— are rich in proteins of many kinds, and no organism has been found

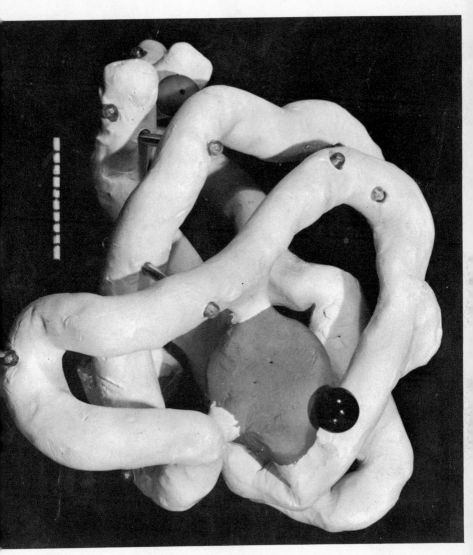

1   A model of a protein molecule—myoglobin, a protein present in muscle and other tissues, which serves as an oxygen store. Polypeptide chains are white; the grey disc is the haem group. The small spheres are marker atoms attached to the molecule. Marks on the scale are 1 Angstrom Unit (10^{-8} cm.) apart. (Photograph by Dr J. C. Kendrew)

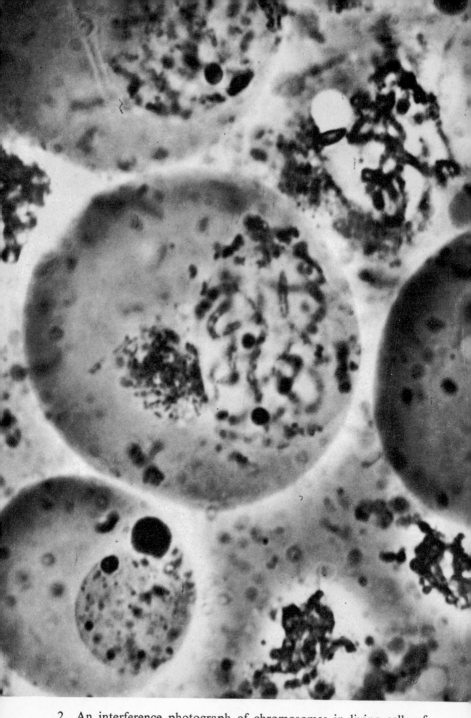

2 An interference photograph of chromosomes in living cells of *Schistocerea gregaria* (grasshopper). (From *Proc. Royal Soc.*, by permission of Mr E. J. Ambrose)

which does not contain protein in every part. We are justified in regarding proteins as the characteristic typical substances of life.

The constitution of proteins, therefore, became a matter of great interest. It was found that they are composed of simpler substances, known as *amino acids*. The characteristic feature of these compounds is that they contain both 'acidic' and 'basic' parts.[1] Because of this they are capable of uniting with each other, the basic group of one amino acid combining with the acidic group of another. (Fig. 1.) The

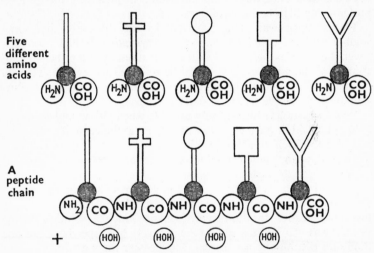

FIG. 1. A diagrammatic representation of the molecules of five different amino acids, showing how they combine together (with the elimination of water, HOH) to form a peptide chain. This is the basic structure of proteins. The different characteristic groups of the amino acids are represented by conventional signs. For their chemical formulae see Appendix 1

amino acids have, as it were, two hands: an acidic hand and a basic hand. Suppose all the acidic hands wear red gloves and all the basic hands wear black gloves; then the protein can be pictured as like a row of people in which every hand with a red glove clasps his neighbour's black glove.

In this way long chains of amino acid groups are formed. As there are found in proteins about twenty separate kinds of amino acids, which can be joined together in this way, it is easy to see that the number of ways in which they can be arranged is almost endless. It is thus possible to have a very large number of different 'chains' of amino

[1] The acid group is CO.OH and the basic group H_2N

B

acids, according to the proportions of the amino acids which they contain and the order in which they come.

The study of proteins was delayed because their molecules were found to be very much larger than the molecules with which the chemist had been accustomed to deal. This presented problems of purification of a novel kind, and for a long time it was not known whether typical proteins were composed of many molecules of one kind or were mixtures of numerous different molecules. This could not be settled until ways were discovered of analysing mixtures of proteins into their component parts.

This analysis was greatly assisted by the discovery that some soluble proteins could be induced to *crystallize*. It had been discovered by Hofmeister, in 1890, that egg albumin, the principal constituent of the white of eggs, could be obtained as crystals. The red pigment of the blood of animals had also been obtained in a crystalline state by very simple means as early as 1867.

Now a crystalline form is only possible when all the molecules are either identical or have very similar shapes. So the crystallization of a protein is by itself an act of purification and means that we have obtained a substance in which all the particles are either the same, or at least very similar in size and shape.

Physical methods of studying the molecules of proteins were also developed. Professor The Svedberg of Uppsala, Sweden, invented an instrument called the 'ultracentrifuge' in which a solution of the protein was whirled in a small tube at a very high speed—about one thousand revolutions per second. The heavier the particle, the more rapidly does it move away from the centre of rotation under the influence of the centrifugal force. From the rate of movement, which could be observed by a rather complicated optical arrangement, it was possible to deduce the weights of the molecules of proteins.

In these experiments, it was found first that well-purified proteins (and especially those which had been crystallized) were composed of molecules of the same size. Secondly, the weights of the molecules of proteins were much greater than those of simple organic substances like sugar, which chemists were accustomed to handle. Taking the weight of the hydrogen atom as unity, simple organic substances like alcohol or sugar have molecular weights between 50 and 200. Larger molecules had been made with weights up to a thousand or even more, but with proteins molecular weights of many thousands are common. One of the simplest protein-like substances known is insulin, with a molecular weight of about 5,000. But most protein molecules are much larger than this and have weights of 60,000-100,000, while in others the molecular weight is a million or more. Fig. 2 shows the comparative sizes of some protein molecules and some of the larger particles we shall meet later.

It is evident that the task of determining how the constituent amino acids are arranged in molecules of this magnitude is a very difficult one. Up to the present it has only been completely achieved in the one case of insulin, which has been studied by Dr F. Sanger, of Cambridge. Analysis showed that the molecule of insulin contained

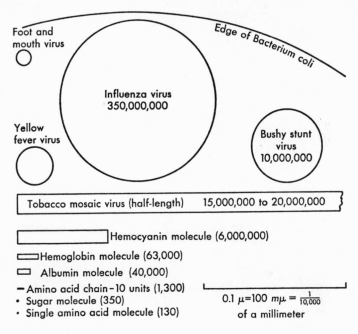

FIG. 2. Relative sizes of molecules of simple substances and proteins and of virus particles and bacteria

fifty-one amino acids of fifteen different kinds. These were arranged in two distinct chains, one containing twenty-one amino acids and the other with thirty amino acids. The exact order of the amino acids in both of these chains have been determined by Dr Sanger and is shown in Fig. 3. The two chains are joined together in two places by cystine, which contains sulphur, through which the junction is made.

Insulin is a protein which is extracted from the pancreas of animals. It is of great importance because it is involved in the utilization of sugar in the body. The human disease, diabetes—an inability

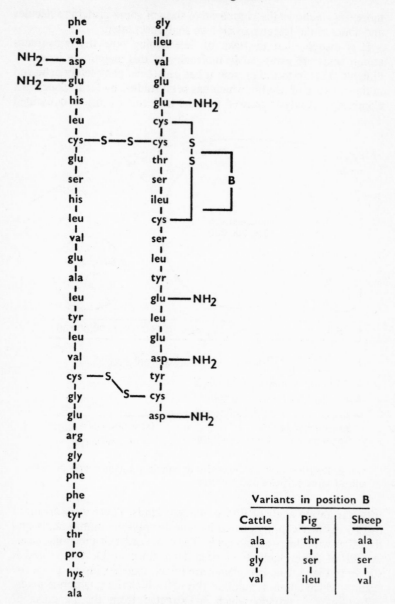

FIG. 3. The arrangement of the fifty-one amino acids in the molecule of pig insulin (for full names, see Appendix, p. 162). Insulins from other species differ slightly in the short section marked B. asp—NH₂ is asparigine and glu—NH₂ is glutamine.

to utilize sugar, which then accumulates in the blood—is due to a deficiency of insulin. It is well known that this deficiency in human beings can be made good by injecting insulin of animal origin; and for this reason large quantities of animal insulins are prepared.

Sanger's experiments showed that the arrangement of amino acids in beef insulin is quite unique. Every molecule has the same amino acids in precisely the same order. Experiments have also shown that a very slight modification of insulin, e.g. the removal or modification of only one of the amino acids, may spoil its activity as an anti-diabetic agent. When a comparison was made of insulins prepared from different species, the ox, pig and sheep, they were found to be very similar, differing only in a small section of three amino acids only, in which some variation of the insulins from different sources was found.[1]

We meet here one of the most characteristic features of living organisms—their ability to construct long protein chains, in which the order of the amino acids is precisely maintained. We shall see that this ability is the basic characteristic of living things, which enables them to make the large numbers of highly specific and exactly constructed proteins which they need for their purposes.

Plate 1 shows a model of a much more complicated protein, myo-globin, which contains several peptide chains, as worked out by Dr J. C. Kendrew.

[1] The variations are in the section of chain marked B which is bridged by -S-S- (Fig. 3), i.e. in the positions 8, 9 and 10 from the top.

II

How the Cell Lives

꒰ꑀ꒱

Before we go any further, we must consider a little what goes on inside the living cell. All living cells are necessarily the seat of intense chemical activity. In order to live they must have food, which enters into the cell and is transformed in various ways. It may be burnt to provide energy or changed into substances needed for growth, and the products which are not wanted are given out.

Plants are extremely modest in their requirements. From carbon dioxide taken from the atmosphere, water and simple inorganic nutrients, which contain nitrogen, phosphorus and a few more inorganic elements, they are able, with the help of the energy of light, to construct all the chemical compounds, including proteins, which they require. Animal cells have to be provided with a greater variety of foods. As a rule they require, at least, the simpler compounds synthesized in plants; but from these they obtain what they need to live. From the oxidation of sugars they obtain the energy which is required to keep them alive. While single living cells like bacteria are able to carry out all the processes necessary for living, in higher organisms there is some specialization, i.e. some cells perform one task and others mainly another.

It is obvious that the life of all cells involves a multitude of chemical actions which are carried and with a speed and smoothness which the laboratory chemist cannot approach. In practice, chemical synthesis in the laboratory is often very difficult. Compounds have to be transformed one step at a time, often by wasteful processes, using powerful chemicals, heat, and sometimes electrical actions, to bring about the desired changes. It may take months to build up a compound, by a complicated sequence of actions, which a cell can make in a matter of minutes. Many bacteria completely reproduce themselves in half an hour, and in that time everything they contain is duplicated.

How are these manifold changes brought about? We will take a simple living thing—the yeast cell—a unicellular organism which causes fermentation of sugar. It is a jelly-like bag, containing a viscous sticky fluid. It is in this fluid that the chemical changes take place. Yeast will grow in a liquid containing a few simple compounds like sugar, nitrogen compounds, phosphate, and a few other essential nutrients. These enter the cell through its skin or membrane, and when inside are transformed into many other compounds. The nitrogen compounds are built up into the proteins required for growth and reproduction, the sugars are partly elaborated into more complex carbohydrates and partly burnt to provide the energy required for the other transformations, yielding either carbon dioxide or alcohol, according to the circumstances.

This property of yeast was discovered in the early stages of pastoral civilization. The carbon dioxide was used to leaven the dough in the baking of bread; and the production of alcohol has been used for the manufacture of alcoholic drinks from time immemorial.

If you were to ask a chemist to take sugar and turn it into alcohol, he could do it, but only with great difficulty and through a long and complex series of changes. In fact most of the alcohol of commerce is manufactured by the fermentation of sugars by the humble yeast cell. How does it bring about this change with such surprising ease? At one time it was thought that only the living cells could bring about such changes, which were connected with the essential vital activity of the cell. Then a German chemist, Büchner, showed that it was possible to squeeze the juice out of the living cells, and this juice, freed of cell fragments, was capable of fermenting sugar. It contained substances, which he called *enzymes*, which bring about these changes.

Before this, substances which assist chemical change had been discovered and called *catalysts*; for example, platinum, which makes hydrogen and oxygen combine. Enzymes were evidently vital catalysts or *bio-catalysts*; but for many years, indeed until quite recently, their nature has been quite unknown. Many chemists tried unsuccessfully to purify and isolate them. They were found to be both varied and ubiquitous.

Before we examine their nature, let me gives a few examples of enzymes. When food passes through the digestive tract of animals, it encounters enzymes throughout its passage which break it down and make it suitable for absorption. In the stomach there is pepsin, which begins the break-down of proteins. Into the intestine, the pancreas pours other enzymes, which continue the digestion of protein and break down starch into sugars, digest the fats and so on. A very large number of enzymes, which facilitate a multitude of chemical changes, have been distinguished in every kind of living organism and no doubt there are many others to be discovered. All living things contain them, not only in their digestive organs, but also in every tissue. The sap of the growing plant contains a host of them. Even in the seed there are enzymes packed away, which will act on the starch when germination begins and produce the .sugar which feeds the plant until it has roots and leaves.

A large number of enzymes are also concerned with the oxidation of carbohydrates. When conducted in the cell this is by no means a simple process like the burning of wood. In the cell it is necessary that the energy given out on oxidation should be obtained in a form in which it is available for use. A great deal of work has been done to elucidate the very complex sequence of reactions which occur. The main result has been to find that the oxidation processes are coupled with reactions involving phosphates, as the result of which 'high-energy' phosphate compounds are formed. In these compounds the energy is available for bringing about the reactions which the cell has to perform, and they are also used in muscle cells in the processes by which mechanical work is performed.

What are the enzymes which have these remarkable properties? In 1926, Professor J. B. Sumner, of Ithaca, obtained from jack beans a crystalline substance which had the property of breaking down urea. It appeared to be the enzyme called *urease*, and further investigation has confirmed this. It was the first enzyme to be prepared in a crystalline condition as a pure substance, so that its nature could be determined. It was found to be a *protein*. Since then a considerable number of enzymes has been isolated and many have been obtained in the crystalline state. Pepsin, the protein-splitting enzyme of the stomach, was crystallized by Dr J. H. Northrop at Princeton in 1929. Later the animal pancreas was found to be a rich mine of proteins, and Drs Northrop and Kunitz and their collaborators isolated from it a succession of crystalline enzymes, such as trypsin and chymotrypsin, which are poured into the intestine and complete the digestion of the food. Enzymes have also been isolated from varied materials such as yeast, malt, potatoes, fruit juices and milk.

All these substances are very powerful bio-catalysts, i.e. they bring about rapid chemical changes when present in very small amounts, without being changed themselves. A solution containing a ten millionth of an ounce of pepsin has a powerful effect on clotting of milk; rennin, another enzyme present in calves' stomachs and used for making junkets and cheese, can clot ten million times its weight of milk in ten minutes. Urease crystals produce a hundred times their weight of ammonia from urea in five minutes; it is said that one molecule of catalase can decompose over two million molecules of hydrogen peroxide every minute.

All these enzymes turned out to be proteins. In this way it became evident that besides their other functions, Nature makes use of proteins as 'biocatalysts'. Enzymes are indeed highly specialized agents. There is usually a separate enzyme for each distinct chemical process. Sometimes an enzyme will bring about the change in a single substance only; but others are capable of changing a number of closely related substances.

Very little is known about how enzymes bring about these chemical actions. It has been shown that the first step is the combination of the enzyme with the substance undergoing change. This combination is very specific. The enzyme will combine with one, or perhaps a few similar molecules, but with no others. There must thus be a close fit between the enzyme and the molecule or molecules it acts on. The molecules must fit exactly into some part of the surface of the enzyme molecule.

What happens then is largely a matter of conjecture, but it is not difficult to see that if the enzyme is combined firmly with the two halves of a molecule, the bond joining them may be weakened so that the molecule easily divides into the two halves. The binding of the molecule with the enzyme will necessarily weaken the strength of the bonds holding the molecule together. In this way the enzyme can facilitate the rupture of a molecule into two parts. Readers who are interested will see the idea worked out in more detail in Fig. 4.

The synthesis of a molecule from its parts will also be facilitated if they fit closely into adjacent parts of the enzyme surface, so that they are brought into juxtaposition under conditions in which they will then unite. The enzyme provides a kind of 'jig' which holds the bits together while a bond between them is formed.

In either case the important thing is that the enzyme must provide a structure which is exactly adapted to the molecules it has to deal with.

Life is largely a matter of enzymes. All organisms contain large numbers of them—all working together and bringing about the extraordinary changes which life produces in its environment. Many kinds of them exist in living things. Not only is it found that every organism has a considerable number of enzymes, but it also appears that an enzyme of one species is not exactly the same as an enzyme with similar functions in another. The enzymes are therefore not only highly adapted to the chemical changes they have to bring about; they are also stamped in some way with the individuality of the species they belong to. We do not know how this is achieved.

But in the amino acid chains of proteins, which were described in Chapter I, we have seen that there exists the possibility of almost innumerable different patterns. Nature has apparently taken advantage of this to produce the many specialized patterns of enzymes, but

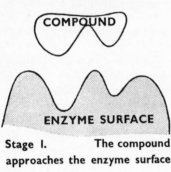

Stage I. The compound approaches the enzyme surface

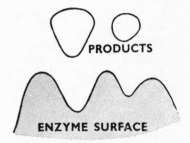

Stage II. The compound combines with the enzyme surface

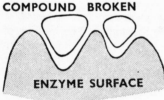

Stage III. The compound is broken into two parts

Stage IV. The products are released from the enzyme surface

FIG. 4. How an enzyme acts. Characteristic of enzyme action is the high degree of specificity, i.e., a close fit between the enzyme and the compound it acts on

at present we are ignorant as to the nature of the patterns which constitute the active groupings in the enzymes.

It is an extraordinary fact—and an unexpected one—that the simplest organisms seem to be provided with enzymes which are very similar to those of the highest organisms. Even the simplest forms of life which have survived to this day have practically all the types of enzymes which we find in the higher animals. It is possible that new types may be discovered in the higher animals but so far we have no clear evidence in favour of this possibility. If life has evolved from simple unicellular organisms to complex ones, there does not seem to have been any great improvement in the enzymes. There has merely been an increase in specialization and in the possibilities of cooperation and of division of labour between cells.

In fact, as we have seen, it is usually the case that the simpler organisms, in order to live, have to carry out a greater range of chemical actions, so that they are very rich in enzymes—perhaps richer than the more highly developed animals.

Let us take a look at a specimen of a very simple organism—a single cell of a small bacterium, of which the solid parts weigh 10^{-13} of a gram (i.e. about 300 million million will make up one ounce). In this tiny volume it can be calculated that there will be about 200,000 protein molecules altogether. A moderate estimate suggests that the bacterium must have several hundred distinct enzymes at least for all its activities, or perhaps a thousand or more. Obviously there cannot be very many molecules of each enzyme—an average of 200 or so of each, but in some cases perhaps there will only be a few molecules of a particular enzyme.

Our picture of the smallest living cells is thus already one of a complexity which the mind finds difficulty in grasping. How all these separate and complex enzyme molecules are packed away in a tiny fragment of protoplasm, how they work in harmony with each other, producing that result which we recognize as life, we hardly know. How they are made out of the food which the organism lives on, we shall discuss in a later chapter.

III

Vitamins and Antivitamins

It would be wrong to give the impression that living things contain only proteins. An enormous number of smaller molecules have been found, usually in rather small quantities, in living tissues. They are the intermediates, the partly completed structures which will eventually enter into the larger aggregates, or the messengers which go to and fro, carrying energy or otherwise facilitating the working of the machinery of the cells.

The organisms make many of these substances themselves, but different organisms differ enormously in their ability to synthesize compounds. Some, like plants, can create everything they need from very simple nutrients—a few inorganic salts, ammonia or nitrate, phosphate and carbon dioxide from the air. General speaking, the higher an organism is in scale of complexity, the less is its synthetic ability. Micro-organisms usually have much greater power of synthesis than animals, but even they are found to differ greatly in their nutritional requirements. Some are perhaps even less exacting than the plants; for example, the nitrogen-fixing bacteria which exist in nodules of leguminous plants have the ability to use the nitrogen directly from the air.

The basic food requirements of the higher animals are certain inorganic materials like salt, phosphate, calcium, iron (the *mineral* elements of diet), proteins or their constituent parts, from which they are able to build new protein, and carbohydrates, and perhaps also some fat as sources of energy. It was found, however, in many laboratories engaged in nutritional studies that animals fed with what appeared to be completely satisfactory diets, containing all these constituents in a purified form but nothing else, failed to grow and often developed severe symptoms of disease.

One of the earliest experiments of this kind was made in 1912 by Sir Frederick Gowland Hopkins. He found that young rats would not grow properly on a diet made from the purified constituents of milk, but even small quantities of whole natural milk restored the rate of growth. Much earlier than this, disease in both humans and animals were suspected to be due to deficiencies of diet. Beri-beri, a disease of the Orient, which was prevalent in the Japanese navy up to 1882, was almost eliminated by a change of diet involving a reduction of the amount of rice consumed. Eijkman in 1897 found that hens and pigeons fed on white polished rice developed a type of paralysis, which disappeared when the rice polishings were added to the diet. The inference was that the polishings contained something necessary for health. Such auxiliary substances were named *vitamins* by Funk, a scientist who tried to separate the essential factor from the rice polishings.

Following the observations of Hopkins, experiments were made to try to distinguish the factor which was present in raw milk, but was not present in the purified milk constituents. It was found in fact that there were two factors, and the lack of either produced growth disorders. The first, which was present in the fat, was called vitamin A, and the second, present in the watery part of the milk, vitamin B. This was the beginning of the discovery of the vitamins, and since that time at least thirty such substances which are necessary, in small quantities, for the growth of various animals have been distinguished.

Many of them have been isolated in the pure form and their chemical structures have been determined, and in many cases this has been followed by their synthesis by chemists. The first to be identified and reconstructed in the laboratory was vitamin C. It had been known for many years that people who lived for a considerable time on a diet which contained no fresh vegetables or fruit juices developed scurvy. Vitamin C was identified by Szent Gyorgyi with a substance called ascorbic acid which is present in large amounts in pepper, and it was then synthesized chemically by Sir Norman Haworth and his co-workers.

Another somewhat similar deficiency disease was pellagra, which was common in the southern part of the United States among the poorer people whose diet was mainly corn meal, sugar, molasses, and sometimes pork. Elvehjem discovered in 1937 that pellagra could be cured in a few days by a substance called nicotinic acid or niacin.

Hopkins suggested, as long ago as 1906, that rickets was a deficiency disease, and it was found that cod liver oil had an excellent effect. The active substance, which was called vitamin D, has been shown to consist of a group of rather similar complex molecules called *sterols*. Sterols exist in many foods, as well as in skin, in an inactive form, and it has been found that if this is exposed to a source of ultra-violet light, such as bright sunlight, out of doors, the active vitamin is formed. This is one of the reasons why sunshine is health-giving.

Vitamin B has been found to contain quite a number of different substances, many of which have been identified and some synthesized. Vitamin B1, now called aneurin or thiamine, is the substance of which a deficiency causes beri-beri. B2 was identified by Kuhn and Karrer with riboflavin, a substance present in milk, eggs, or liver, the lack of which produces dermatitis, facial sores, etc. B3 is possibly a substance called pantothenic acid, which was first found to be required by yeasts and later recognized as a food requirement of animals and insects. B6 was identified with pyridoxine in 1938, and in 1944 a more active form of the vitamin was discovered in the compound pyridoxal.

Other substances which are essential to the life and growth of many organisms are choline, a simple substance required by rats and birds and possibly by human beings; biotin, originally recognized as a food requirement of yeasts, but since known to be required by the higher animals; inositol, a particular type of sugar, and folic acid, a substance abundantly present in green leaves, which stimulates growth.

Having discovered all these substances, which must be present in our food in minute quantities, to keep us healthy, working organisms, scientists naturally began to wonder what their action is. If the lack of them produces such serious effects, they must perform a very vital function.

The clue to this came from quite a different direction. It will be remembered that the juice squeezed out of living yeast cells contains enzymes which can by themselves ferment sugars. It was discovered by Harden and Young in 1906 that if this juice was divided into two parts, one containing the big (protein) molecules and the other small molecules, neither part separately could bring about the fermentation, but when they were again mixed the fermentation went on as in the original juice. Hence both the big molecules and the smaller molecules were necessary to bring about the fermentation. The big molecules, as we have seen, are proteins and some of them enzymes. The smaller molecules include some which are also needed for enzyme action, and these were called *co-enzymes*.

In the course of time a number of co-enzymes have been separated and distinguished. It has been found that frequently one co-enzyme is shared by several different enzymes. This appears to be a device of Nature to economize materials which are rather scarce. The yeast juice is like a machine-shop containing many large and complicated machines. The tools used by these machines are, however, in short supply, so the management, instead of firmly attaching each tool to a machine, arranges to have them shared, so that each machine can have the use of the tools when needed.

Enzymes are so active that only small quantities of them are required, and it is not surprising that minute quantities of the co-enzymes are also sufficient. Prof H. McIlwain has found that some bacteria only have a few molecules of some of them in each cell.

The co-enzymes are small molecules, and some of them have been purified and their chemical structures ascertained (see Appendix). It has been found that they are closely associated with the vitamins, being either the vitamins themselves or closely related to them. This has been proved in at least eight cases so far, in which the enzyme system with which the vitamin functions has been identified. For example, nicotinic acid is a constituent of the co-enzymes of yeast juice; aneurin (vitamin B1) is required by an enzyme called *carboxylase*; riboflavin (vitamin B2) is the co-enzyme of several coloured enzymes which bring about oxidations in the cell.

The vitamins are required by animals, firstly because they cannot make them themselves, and secondly because they are unable to perform many of the vital processes of life without them. If the vitamin is not present, the corresponding enzyme system is paralysed, and the animal organisms function only imperfectly or not at all.

Micro-organisms such as bacteria and fungi often need the same vitamins which are required by animals. Eight essential substances have been distinguished as essential to the life of micro-organisms—and they all serve as vitamins for the higher animals. They are aneurin (vitamin B1), riboflavin (vitamin B2), pyridoxin (vitamin B6), biotin (vitamin H), pantothenic acid, folic acid, co-enzyme I or its components, and choline. Readers who are interested will find the formulae of these compounds in the Appendix (p. 163). The ability to synthesize these substances is very haphazardly distributed among micro-organisms. Some, like yeasts, have a considerable ability of making vitamins and are in fact rich sources of some of them. The wild mould *Neurospora crassa* needs only glucose, ammonia, and biotin in order to live; all other necessary substances it can make for itself. Other micro-organisms can only grow if they are provided with certain of these substances; they are unable to make them for themselves, and they must have them if they are to grow. It was found that some animals seemed to get along quite well on diets which lacked some of the B vitamins. There was no evidence that the animal itself was capable of synthesizing them. The mystery was solved when it was discovered that the microflora of the animal's digestive tract were manufacturing vitamins and so contributing to the nutrition of their host.

The wide occurrence of vitamins in all kinds of living things is another proof of the essential unity of life. From micro-organisms to man, they are all built on much the same plan. They all have extremely similar enzyme systems, and require the same auxiliary substances. But some organisms are dependent on others for some of these vital substances, as they have lost the power of making their own. Broadly speaking, the higher the organism is in the scale of living things the less is its synthetic ability and its dependence on other forms of life for the compounds it needs is greater.

As I said before, many of the vitamins can now be constructed in the laboratory. Chemists can do more than this. Not only can they construct the actual vitamin, the molecule which has been selected in Nature to do a particular job; they can also make a variety of similar molecules, which may differ from the vitamin in a slightly different arrangement of atoms or in the slight additions here and there, which do not spoil the general plan of the molecule. What happens when an organism is presented with these *pseudo* vitamins? Does it reject them or can it make use of them? Actually it tries to make use of them, but often unsuccessfully. The 'unnatural' vitamin combines with its enzyme. The protein part of the enzyme does not notice that the vitamin is not quite right. It accepts it as a co-enzyme but, alas, the combination does not function properly. As we have seen, enzymes act by achieving a very exact fit with the substances they act on—like the fit of a lock and key. If a part of the enzyme, the co-enzyme for example, is changed slightly, the key will not go into the lock. Moreover, even if the natural vitamin is also present, it may be partly prevented from doing its work, for the unnatural vitamin competes for the available enzyme molecules and put a proportion of them, at least, out of action.

So the result is that 'unnatural' vitamin molecules act as antagonists to the real vitamins. They often prevent the proper functioning of the real vitamin and produce the same symptoms as a severe vitamin deficiency.

This seems to provide a wonderful way of preventing the growth of harmful organisms, like bacteria. All you need do is to introduce a suitable antagonist which will put out of action a vital enzyme in the bacteria, which will then be unable to grow.

Unfortunately, the hosts and the parasites are usually very much alike and possess very similar enzymes, and it is frequently found that they require the same vitamins and respond similarly to their

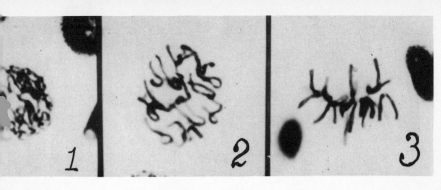

...omosomes are seen ...gle of fine threads

The chromosomes are separating from each other and are thickening

Each chromosome has split into two distinct threads

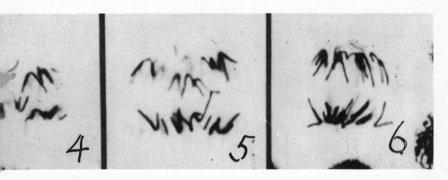

The newly divided chromosomes are moving away from each other

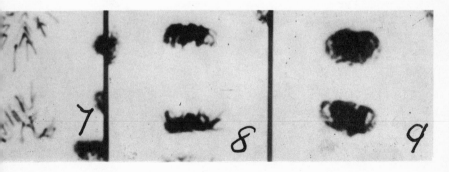

...ets of chromosomes collect together at opposite sides of the cell and cell division takes ... At the end of the process there are two distinct cells. The cell walls are not visible

3   Chromosomes in the nucleus of cells from the growing tip of onion root in different stages of cell division. (Photographs of fixed and stained preparations reproduced by courtesy of Dr S. H. Revell, Chester Beatty Research Institute)

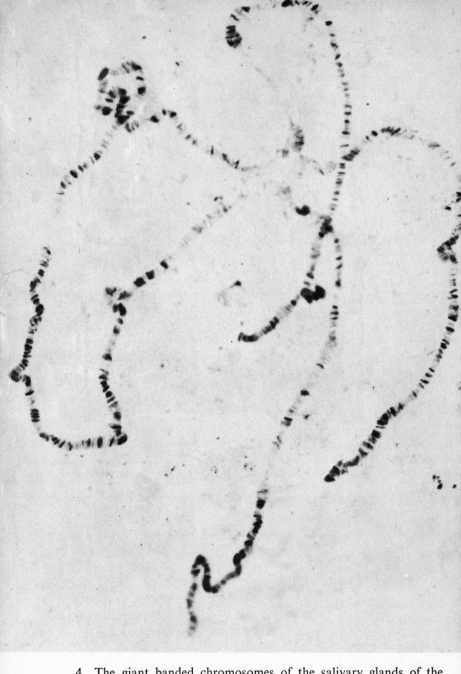

4 The giant banded chromosomes of the salivary glands of the larva of the fly, *Drosophila melanogaster*. In these chromosomes the threads have multiplied side by side so that the final chromosome consists of many similar threads lying alongside each other. (Photograph by Dr O. G. Fahmy)

antagonists. A large number of vitamin antagonists have been made, which do in fact interfere with the growth of bacteria; but in most cases they are nearly as harmful to animals as to the bacteria.

There is, however, one case in which successful use is made of an antagonist, and this is the basis of the well-known 'sulphur' drugs (sulphanilamides). These were discovered by trial and error. Until recent years there was very little to guide chemists in the search for valuable drugs. Enormous numbers of compounds have been made and tested; some had curative properties, but no one knew why. This group of drugs was discovered after long research to be extremely effective in some kinds of infections. The reason for this was not clear at once. Then it was discovered that a somewhat similar substance, *p-amino-benzoic acid* (PAB for short), interfered with the bactericidal action of the drug (for formulae, see Appendix, p. 164). If PAB is administered with the drug, much larger doses have to be used to produce the same effect. This suggested to Fildes and Woods that the 'sulphur' drugs were really antagonists of PAB. At this time PAB had not been recognized as a vitamin, but its presence in many micro-organisms has since been confirmed. It is now known to be a component of folic acid, a substance which occurs abundantly in green leaves and has a stimulating effect on the growth of some bacteria. Folic acid seems to be concerned in the formation of the highly specialized substances required in the nuclei of cells. The higher animals as well as many of the lower organisms require PAB; but it is not known definitely why certain bacteria are more sensitive to PAB antagonists than are the hosts. More recently it has been found that another compound of the same kind (PAS = *p.-amino-salicylic acid*) is very effective in arresting some types of tuberculosis.

If it were possible to find enzymes in the disease-producing organisms which were more sensitive to antagonists than those of the animals, the problem of finding drugs to kill the bacteria would be very simple; but unfortunately this is not usually possible. Drugs which harm the parasite usually injure the host as well.

The problem of producing substances which will harm bacteria more than their hosts is one which has been solved more effectively by many organisms than by the conscious efforts of scientists. Many living things must have encountered the problem of how to repel the attacks of bacteria and other parasitic forms, and it is perhaps not surprising that those which have survived are provided with chemical protection. The best known of these substances is *penicillin,* which is produced by a fungus, *Penicillium notatum,* the greenish mould which grows on damp bread. The story of the discovery of penicillin by Sir Alexander Fleming in 1929 has often been told. He noticed

C

that there was a clear patch around a growth of the fungus on a plate on which colonies of bacteria were growing. He recognized that the fungus was producing a substance which prevented the growth of the bacteria. The isolation and identification of this substance, as the result first of the efforts of a group of workers headed by Sir Howard Florey and Professor Chain in Oxford and the co-operative effort of scientists on both sides of the Atlantic during the 1939-45 war, and its large-scale production and use in medicine have been one of the greatest triumphs of intensive research. Penicillin is unique in having an extremely powerful effect on some types of bacteria and in doing no harm to animals, and is one of the most powerful means of combating many kinds of bacteria which is available at the present time. The nature of its action is not clearly understood.

But many other 'antibiotics', as they are called, have also been discovered in recent years. Many of them are too harmful to human beings to find use in medicine. Others, like gramicidin, and streptomycin, both prepared from soil bacteria, are extremely useful.

Streptomycin, which is produced by a micro-organism first isolated from the soil of a field near Caracas in Venezuela, seems to be effective in some cases of tuberculosis. This family of micro-organisms (*Streptomyces*)—in this case a type isolated from a compost heap in Illinois—has also yielded *chloromycetin*, which has been found to be a most successful curative agent for typhus—a louse-carried fever which is common in overcrowded conditions in the tropics. It almost completely fulfils the two requirements of an effective drug—it is deadly against the agent of the disease, and harmless to the human body. Although it is also effective against some bacteria, it is of great interest because typhus is a virus disease and this is the first drug to be discovered which is effective in such cases. Virus diseases have hitherto been very refractory to treatment by chemical agents, so that this discovery opens up great possibilities of new treatments. Chloromycetin has been found to be a comparatively simple compound and has been synthesized. Another useful agent of the same type is known as *aureomycin* or *duomycin*, which is very effective in rocky mountain fever and other virus diseases of the same type.

All these substances may be similar to fragments of proteins—probably warped fragments, which will not fit into the normal protein molecule.

Competition in the world of micro-organisms, which multiply at a very rapid rate, must be very intense, and any species which can produce something which kills, or merely prevents the multiplication of, organisms in its neighbourhood, secures for itself the chance to multiply. Such substances, which may have been produced originally by the faulty working of a single cell, would immediately be of value to the organism, and would ensure its survival. It is not surprising that in the innumerable generations through which they must have passed in the course of ages, the micro-organisms have been found effective chemical weapons for self-preservation. At one time or another individuals which are faulty in some way may produce unusual chemical compounds which may be of value in this way.

THE USE OF METALS BY LIVING CELLS

For the want of a nail the kingdom was lost—Nursery Rhyme

Vitamins are not the only minerals, besides the basic amino acids, which are required in constructing the large molecules of living cells. Life seems to have explored every possibility and has made use somewhere or other of nearly every material available on the surface of the earth. The common metals sodium, potassium, and calcium are ubiquitous. There are a fair number of proteins which contain other metals. Iron, for example, is an important constituent of haemoglobin, the red protein of the blood of mammals. The iron, present in a particular combination, enables the haemoglobin to pick up oxygen in the lungs and to carry it into the tissues, where it is released. Lobsters and other crustaceans offer a variation on the same theme. Their respiratory protein contains copper instead of iron, and as a result their blood is literally blue.

Even more extraordinary is the fact that *Ascidia* (star fish) have green, blue, and orange corpuscles in their blood, as well as colourless ones. The coloured ones contain appreciable quantities of vanadium, although its concentration in the sea water in which they live is so small it cannot be detected by any known test. Other types of animal, the beautiful annelid worms called *Sabellids* and *Serpulids*, have green blood, the colour of which is due to a haemoglobin-like protein called *chlorocruorin*.

Plant life uses the same kind of compound in chlorophyll—the all-important pigment of green leaves—but the metal is now magnesium. It might be thought that the difference represents the great division between animal and plant life, the animals being based taking haemoglobin or similar oxygen-carrying proteins and the plants using chlorophyll: but as a matter of fact haemoglobin-like proteins have been detected in the nitrogen-fixing nodules of leguminous plants. So it would appear that both chlorophyll proteins and haemoglobins were present before the division into plant and animal life took place, but plants have relied increasingly on chlorophyll and many of them have lost ability to make haemoglobin-like proteins.

Enzymes have also been isolated which contain copper, zinc, manganese, iron, and vanadium. The amount of the metal in the enzyme is usually quite small, less than 1 per cent, and as only small quantities of the enzymes are present in the tissues, the amounts of the metals used in this way are very small—mere traces are sufficient to satisfy the needs of organisms. Living things usually get what they need without any difficulty, but sometimes the supply falls below the level required.

It has been found in experiments with plants growing in carefully purified solutions, that iron, manganese, boron, copper, and zinc are essential for plant growth, at concentrations of less than one part in a million. No more than this is necessary, and much larger quantities may be harmful. If the soil is seriously deficient in any of the metals, plant growth suffers. but it can be improved by making good the deficiency. Thus, the application of manganese and zinc compounds to marshland fields in Kent increased the yield of potatoes from seven to eleven tons per acre. In south-east Australia there is an extensive coastal strip in which a copper deficiency limits vegetation. Oats, wheat, and lucerne all failed without added copper, but grew luxuriantly when a copper salt was added to the soil. Further inland, zinc is also needed, but extra copper was also required before the clover would set seed. It has been found that plants often grow quite well without much copper up to blossoming time, but seed formation is interfered with. The effect of copper on clover growth is greater if the copper salt is applied a season in advance, due apparently to its effect on nitrification bacteria. Fruit trees, which will not fruit, have been made to do so by inserting capsules of a manganese salt into holes bored into the trunks.

Even when plants can grow well, they do not always satisfy the mineral requirements of the animals feeding on them. Diseases due to cobalt—and copper—deficiencies in sheep and cattle are well known in various regions. In Scotland and Australia sheep 'pining' occurs on soils with less than five parts per million of cobalt. It has been found that this condition is remedied if cobalt, together with copper, in the form of salts, of course, is added to the food. Apparently only ruminants suffer from this deficiency; horses, kangaroos, and rabbits do quite well under the same conditions.

Copper is utilized, rather oddly, in putting the 'crimp' into sheep's wool. If the herbage is deficient in copper, the wool grows straight. The reason, apparently, is that the molecules of the wool protein are first formed in a straight parallel form. The 'crimp' is produced when the long protein chains are joined by -S-S- bonds, an operation performed by an enzyme containing copper. It has also been found that black sheep are unable to grow black wool on a copper-deficient diet, a copper enzyme being the agent of the formation of the black pigment.

Another not very common metal which is found in many living organisms is molybdenum. It has been found recently that this is required for certain enzyme systems, particularly xanthine oxidase, which is concerned with the breakdown of 'purines' and performs a step in a series of reactions which ultimately leads to their excretion as uric acid. Xanthine oxidase is present in quite appreciable quantities in cows' milk.

Until recently it was not known in what substances the animals made use of cobalt, but in 1948 two teams of workers, one headed by Dr Lester Smith in England and the other by Dr Rickes in New Jersey, isolated a cobalt-containing substance (sometimes known as vitamin B12 from the liver; this substance ameliorates pernicious anaemia. If the animal is unable to make enough of this substance, red blood cells are not manufactured in the marrow. But injecting sheep with either a cobalt salt or this pernicious anaemia factor, did not cure the deficiency condition. Cobalt taken by the mouth is effective, but not if injected directly into the blood. It was therefore thought that even in cobalt-deficient pastures, sheep get enough cobalt to make the anti-anaemic factor; but insufficient to satisfy the micro-organisms which play so large a part in the digestive apparatus of ruminants.

How the micro-organisms use cobalt is not known at present; but it may be that they synthesize for their own purposes compounds similar to the pernicious anaemia factor. In fact this substance has been isolated from a mould *Streptomyces griseus*—the same one which yielded streptomycin. What an astonishing thing! After years of great effort, scientists succeed in isolating, from liver, the substance which is necessary for the formation of red blood corpuscles in the bone marrow. No sooner is it isolated than it is also discovered as the product of a mould.

If all this is correct, the emaciation and eventual death of the animals on cobalt-deficient pastures is due to the lack of a milligram or so of cobalt daily, which is apparently required in the enzyme systems of certain micro-organisms, which synthesize vitamins or other substances required by the animal in small amounts. The whole situation rather reminds one of the disastrous consequences of the loss of a nail in the nursery rhyme—but in this case the nail is a cobalt one, which is required as a necessary part of the structure of an essential vitamin.

IV

Cell Division

At this point it is necessary to introduce another great family of substances, which are important constituents of all living cells, *viz.* the nucleic acids. They are so called because they were first found in the cell nucleus—a specialized part of many cells which contains thread-like bodies called chromosomes. They were given this name because they can be stained by certain dyes and made visible. However, in recent years optical techniques have been developed which enable the chromosomes to be photographed in living cells (see Plate 2).

There is no doubt that the chromosomes are intimately concerned with the processes of cell division, whereby a single cell becomes two cells, because they undergo changes during cell division which suggest that they either control the whole process or are an essential part of it.

Just before the cell is ready to divide, the contents of the nucleus can be seen, rather indistinctly, as a tangle of fine threads. They become thicker and more definite and finally collect themselves into distinct chromosomes. At a later stage in the processes (see Plate 3), each chromosome is seen to be split into two threads more or less parallel with each other. The members of each pair move away from each other and finally collect together at opposite sides of the cell.

In this process, the original set of chromosomes is duplicated, so that when the cell divides into two, giving two daughter cells, each contains a complete set of chromosomes like the original cell. It is not surprising that cytologists see in this process the basic mechanism of cell division, which ensures that each new cell has in it a full set of the chromosomes. Later workers on genetics were able to correlate the behaviour of the chromosomes with the laws of heredity, so that they regarded the chromosomes as the carriers of the unit hereditary characters called *genes*. The genes were believed to be arranged in a linear order along the chromosomes and in some cases (particularly

n the salivary glands from the fruit fly larva, which have enormous
hromosomes with a banded structure [Plate 4] can be identified
ith a particular place in the chromosome.

The process just described is that of simple cell division. It is a
ommon method by which unicellular organisms multiply and it
ccurs in the growth of larger organisms. Sexual reproduction is

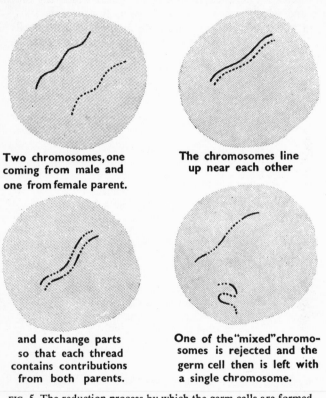

Two chromosomes, one
coming from male and
one from female parent.

The chromosomes line
up near each other

and exchange parts
so that each thread
contains contributions
from both parents.

One of the "mixed" chromosomes is rejected and the
germ cell then is left with
a single chromosome.

FIG. 5. The reduction process by which the germ cells are formed

more complicated. The organism sets aside germ cells, *viz.* the
perm in the male and the egg in the female, which unite in fertiliza-
ion. In the ordinary body cells of the organism there are *two* of
ach kind of chromosome, one coming from the male parent and one
rom the female. When these germ cells are formed, this number is
educed to one by a process of reduction (see Fig. 5). This is itself a
ery wonderful provision which ensures that the chromosomes in the
erm cells contain parts derived from both parents. The two similar

chromosomes line up close to each other and exchange parts with
each other. A new chromosome is then formed which contains parts
from each of the original pair of chromosomes. This remarkable
process, which is known as crossing over, ensures that the single
chromosome of the germ cell contains parts from both parents, but
as the exchange can take place in many different ways, each germ
cell contains a different selection of the genes which the individual
carries and which it has received from its two parents.

When fertilization occurs, the male and female germ cells unite

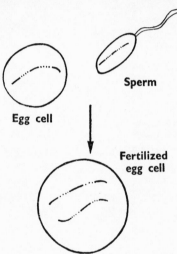

FIG. 6. Fertilization of the egg by the
sperm restores two chromosomes of
each kind to each cell (only one
chromosome in each germ cell is
shown)

and the normal number of chromosomes of each kind—two—in the
cell is then restored. (Fig. 6.) A new individual is formed by many
divisions of the fertilized cell. In every division each chromosome is
replicated, so that every cell of the new organism contains two of
each kind of chromosome, which have been derived from the two
parents. This continues to be the case until the germ cells of the new
individual are formed, when the reduction process occurs again,
which again mixes in a single chromosome the genes derived from
both parents.

This device, which permits two parents to contribute to the
heredity of a single individual, seems to have a crucial one for the

development of the higher organisms. In simple cell division, all lines of descent are distinct; any change occurring in a cell which improves its chance of survival, can only affect its own lineal descendants. In sexual reproduction, every individual has many ancestors. It may seem a very small change to have two parents instead of one; but the effect over a number of generations is overwhelming. If one individual receives contributions to his genes from two parents, four grandparents, and eight great grandparents, it is easy to see that the number of ancestors, say twenty or thirty generations back, which may be represented in one or more of the genes, may be enormous.

Ancestral trees which show the 'descendants' of an individual are extremely misleading. They leave out a great many of the collateral ancestors of succeeding generations. They would be much more informative if written backwards, so that a man or woman could see who are his four grandparents, his eight great-grandparents, and so on, up to 1,048,576 ancestors of the twentieth generation. Even allowing for a considerable amount of duplication, as for example the likelihood that not all these lines of descent are distinct, it is obvious that most of us are descended from practically the whole population of our country twenty generations back, or a mere five or six hundred years ago.

It is not difficult to see that sexual reproduction is in the long run a very effective device for spreading and uniting all the useful and desirable characteristics in a population. The fact that all the higher forms of life use sexual reproduction shows that it has been an important factor in their development.

In the chromosomal filaments we come near to the core of the processes of life. Strung along them are the genes which we must regard as molecular patterns which are capable of

(1) maintaining their identity through many generations of living things,

(2) of being duplicated in the processes of cell division,

(3) of controlling the processes whereby a new individual is formed from a fertilized cell.

We may now ask what is the nature of the substance which has these properties. It was discovered by Miescher in 1871 that the nuclei of cells contain a substance which he called nucleic acid. It was not a protein, but a phosphate of a particular and, at the time, a rather unusual, kind of sugar, called deoxyribose. The whole compound is called *deoxyribonucleic acid*, abbreviated to DNA. The sugar and phosphate groups occur in equal numbers and it is now known that they are arranged in long chains, consisting of alternate phosphate and sugar groups (Fig. 7). In addition each sugar molecule has an organic 'base' attached to it, of which there are commonly four kinds, known as guanine (G), adenine (A), cytosine (C) and thymine (T). It was at first thought that these four bases were present in equal amounts, but careful analyses by Chargaff and others established that this is not so, but they do occur in pairs, i.e. the amount of adenine is always equal to the amount of thymine and the amount of guanine is equal to the amount of cytosine.

The reason for this was discovered by Crick and Watson in the fact that DNA is made up of two threads in which the adenine of one is always paired with thymine in the other and, similarly, guanine in one thread is always paired with thymine in the other (see Fig. 8).

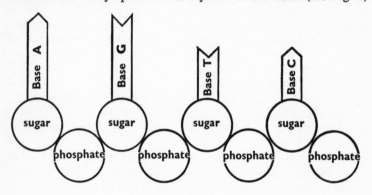

FIG. 7. Chemical composition of one thread of deoxyribonucleic acid

They can do this because their chemical structures are exactly complementary. Guanine can combine in a regular twin-threaded structure with cytosine and only with cytosine, and the same is true of adenine and thymine.[1]

In the structure proposed by Crick and Watson, the two threads are wound round each other to form a spiral, but this is probably not an important feature.

What is much more important is that this structure provides a basis for the reduplication of threads having bases in any particular order. This is because, when they are combined in the way I have described, each thread is the exact complement of the other, i.e. wherever there is A in one thread, there is T in the other and wherever there is G there is C in the other.

A chromosome contains a large number of particles of DNA and it is tempting to identify each one with an independent gene. At the

[1] See Appendix (p. 165) for chemical formulae.

present time this identification cannot be made with certainty, but there is no doubt that one chromosome contains many genes and also many particles of DNA. We might ask how they are assembled in the chromosome. The results of genetics requires that they should be arranged in a linear order, i.e. in one long line. How the individual particles are joined up is not precisely known, but it is known that the DNA is not the sole constituent of the chromosomes. They also contain some rather specialized kinds of protein called protamines (present in fish sperm) and histones (present in many mammalian cells). These proteins are of a basic character, i.e. they are capable of combining firmly with the acidic nucleic acid. Their precise function

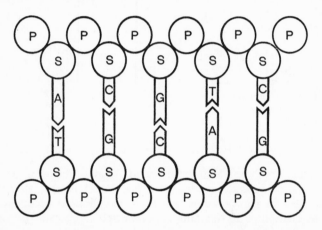

FIG. 8. Double-threaded structure of deoxyribonucleic acid of Crick and Watson

is unknown. It is likely that, by combining with and neutralising the phosphate groups of the DNA, they protect it and perhaps also shield it from other cell chemicals until the time comes for it to function. It is also possible that they are used to effect the junctions between the separate DNA particles. Another possibility, which has been suggested, is that the junctions are effected by the ions of metals such as calcium. However the junction between the individual DNA particles is made, there is no doubt that when the whole chromosome is duplicated, a replica of every DNA particle is formed in the new chromosome.

Experiments have been made using radioactive materials as markers to find in more detail how the replication of the chromosome occurs. The experiments of Taylor and others seem to show that when replication occurs, each new chromosome consists one half of old material and one half of newly synthesized material. This is exactly what would be expected if replication occurs according to the Watson-Crick model, i.e. if each DNA particle divides into two single threads and each half re-forms a complete double thread (see Fig. 9).

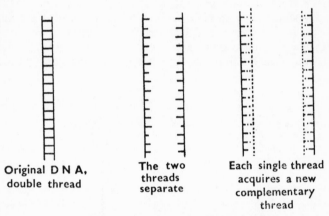

Original D N A,   The two   Each single thread
double thread   threads   acquires a new
                         separate   complementary
                                          thread

FIG. 9. How the DNA particle is reduplicated

All that has to be added to this picture to make it true of the whole chromosome is that the DNA particles should remain attached to each other in a linear order, even when replication occurs, so that the replication of all the individual DNA particles means the replication of the whole chromosome. (Fig. 10.)

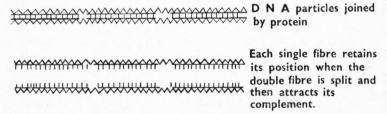

D N A particles joined by protein

Each single fibre retains its position when the double fibre is split and then attracts its complement.

FIG. 10. How the whole chromosome might reduplicate itself

In the whole chromosome the DNA threads must be coiled up and there must also be an apparatus which will pull the new particles apart towards the poles of the cell when cell division occurs. It is possible that the histones are involved to some extent as minute muscles in bringing about these processes, but very little is known of the detailed mechanisms of cell division. However it is brought about, the mechanism is a beautiful example of an intricate mechanism, which functions with great precision. It ensures that when a cell divides into two, not only does one gene of each kind go into the two daughter cells, but they also remain in the same order as in the original cell.[1] Nevertheless very occasionally mistakes happen. A gene may get out of its correct order, or may even be omitted from one of the cells or by accident be reduplicated twice. Such events, as we shall see, may be of great importance in the life of the organism, because they introduce modifications which may sometimes be advantageous.

[1] Dr Lajtha has suggested that the DNA in the chromosome exists as one single continuous thread, which becomes broken into smaller pieces during the processes of preparation of DNA, so that the particle size of the latter, when isolated, does not represent its original condition. However, this view has not been proven.

V

Inside the Cell

꿎

We can now turn our attention from the reproductive apparatus of the nucleus to the other parts of the cell, known as the cytoplasm, in which its ordinary everyday business of living takes place. As we have seen, the cell is a chemical factory which takes in food materials and uses them for its own purposes. One of its needs is energy, which it gets by burning sugars. This requires a whole series of enzymes by which controlled oxidations are performed. As I have already said, these oxidative processes are coupled with other processes which give rise to 'high energy' phosphate compounds. The most important of these is adenosine triphosphate (ATP), which is the main carrier of chemical energy within the organism[1]. It not only provides the energy required for the functioning of muscles, but it also, as we shall see, takes a direct part in the synthetic activities of the cells, including those which give rise to the proteins and nucleic acids.

A typical sugar such as glucose contains six carbon atoms. The first stage is its degradation to two molecules of lactic acid, a 'three-carbon' compound which is oxidized to pyruvic acid. Pyruvic acid is one of the main sources of energy in the cell. The way in which it is used was worked out by Krebs, who showed that it is the fuel of a kind of chemical engine, which operates through a cyclic series of operations known as the *Krebs* or 'citric acid' cycle. The result of this is that the pyruvic acid is oxidized to carbon dioxide and water; while the energy obtained in this process is stored in adenosine triphosphate (ATP), which goes into the pool available for all synthetic processes and for the performance of muscular work.

A rather general picture, due to H. Lettré, showing how this fuel station within the cell operates, is given in Fig. 11. ATP is obtained not only from the oxidation of pyruvic acid, but also, to a lesser extent, from the initial conversion of the sugar to pyruvic acid. No less than

[1] ATP consists of adenine and d-ribose, combined with three molecules of phosphoric acid. See right-hand side of Appendix 1, Fig. 2.

thirty-eight molecules of ATP are formed for the oxidation of one molecule of glucose.

It is of interest to compare the efficiency of the oxidation of fuel in a power station with that in the cell. The overall efficiency of even large mechanical power stations rarely exceeds 15 per cent. Measurements have been made of the yield of ATP from glucose in chopped up pigeon-breast muscle. It was found that at least 70 per

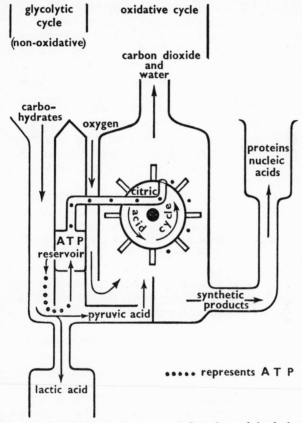

FIG. 11. How the cell obtains its energy. A flow sheet of the fuel station within the cell. (Modified from a diagram by Professor H. Lettré)

cent of the free energy of the glucose was obtained as high-energy ATP: the fuel station in the cell is evidently highly efficient.

But the cell is self-contained. It not only provides its own power supply, but it also uses within itself the energy provided. Some of this energy may be used to perform muscular work, but it is mainly used in chemical operations and these include the manufacture of all the proteins which are necessary to the life of the cell. The cell thus not only has a power station, but it is also continually manufacturing new parts for its own use including the power station 'engines', besides many other mechanisms. The main outcome of all the chemical operations is thus to produce more of the instruments, such as enzymes, which bring about these operations. It is this feature which gives life its militant and aggressive character—living things are always changing their environment, as far as they can, into more living material.

It is obvious that all this chemical activity requires a great deal of organization. However, only very recently has much been learnt about the structure of the cytoplasm in which many of these activities occur, and the way in which the multiple chemical activities are organized so that they are in harmony with each other. The fact that a dead organism soon destroys itself by enzyme degradations is a proof of the existence of co-ordinating factors in living cells.

One of the first explorations of the constituents of cytoplasm was carried out by Dr A. Claude.[1] The walls of the cells were broken by gentle rubbing processes in such a way as to liberate the contents without damaging them severely. The different structures present in the broken cell 'mush' could then be separated according to their size and density by careful centrifuging at different speeds.

The first structure to be deposited is the nucleus, together with cell wall debris, which can be removed. Next come large granules from the cytoplasm, known as *mitochondria*. Then at a still higher speed we can separate submiscroscopic particles, known as *microsomes*. This leaves a 'cell sap' containing some still smaller particles and also proteins and compounds of proteins and nucleic acid, with molecular weights up to a few millions.

This structure of the cell has been confirmed by electron microscope studies of cell sections. The cells are first 'fixed' with a staining material of a heavy metal, osmium, which makes the cell structures visible when the sections are examined in the electron microscope. The cells are then impregnated with a plastic substance, which sets hard and can be cut into very thin slices. Plates 5 and 6 are examples of a cell section, which shows the main structures present. What we have referred to as the microsome appears here as membranes lying parallel with each other in pairs with small massive particles (sub-microsomes) attached to their inner surfaces (see *er* in upper part of Plate 7). Fig. 12 gives a diagrammatic representation of the constitution of a typical cell according to these findings.

[1] Earlier studies had been made by R. R. Bensley and Robert Chambers.

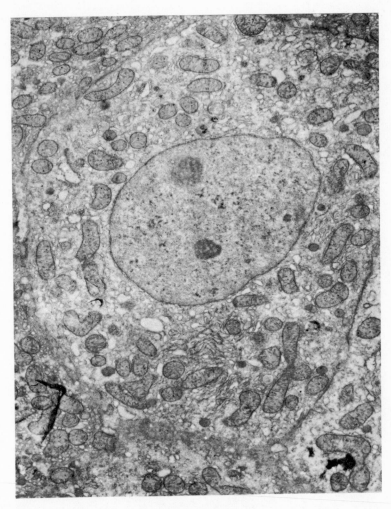

5 A section of rat liver taken with the electron microscope.
(Mr M. S. C. Birbeck.) Magnification ×13,500. The larger central
body is the nucleus. The oval and kidney shaped bodies outside the
nucleus are mitochondria. Below the nucleus can be seen the double
membranes which form the microsomes

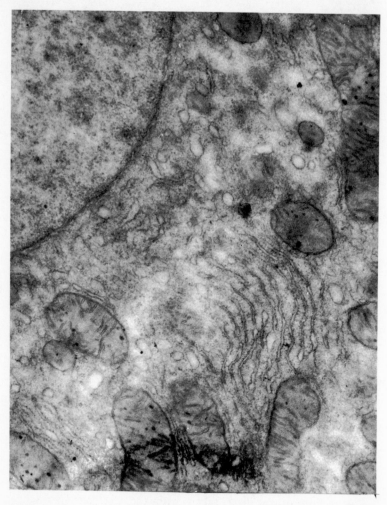

6 A portion of a liver cell taken with the electron microscope at a higher magnification (×48,000) by Mr M. S. C. Birbeck. It shows the oval and kidney shaped mitochondria and also the microsomal membranes

From these experiments we learn that the constituents of the cytoplasm are not all mixed up, but arranged in particles or structures of different kinds. Much work has been done to explore the functions of these particles. It has been found that the mitochondria contain the oxidizing enzymes of the cells. They are in fact the power houses of the cells. The electron microscope has shown them to possess an internal structure of membranes, by means of which the enzyme processes are controlled and organized, but their detailed constitution is still unknown.

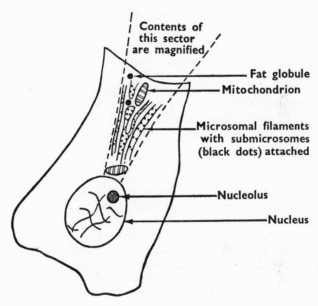

Contents of this sector are magnified

Fat globule
Mitochondrion

Microsomal filaments with submicrosomes (black dots) attached

Nucleolus

Nucleus

FIG. 12. Diagram showing some of the structures usually present in a cell

Mitochondria are relatively large bodies. A typical one is about 2μ long and $\frac{1}{2}\mu$ wide ($1\mu = 1/1000$ of a millimetre) and contains about a million protein molecules of typical size. They appear in the electron microscope pictures (see *m*, Plate 7) to be crossed by thin membranes arranged in pairs. It would seem that the enzymes are organized on these membranes. A considerable number of enzymes is present in a single mitochondrion, to bring about the many chemical changes necessary, but even if there were five hundred distinct enzymes, it would still be possible to have a large number of molecules of each.

D

The small microsomal granules are much smaller. They are about 200 Å (1/100μ), i.e. the diameter is only about one per cent of the average length of the mitochondrion. They are of great interest because they have been found to be the main site of protein synthesis in the cell. They are therefore the central point of the cell's operations—a sort of inner sanctum where the essential components of the cell are formed.

PROTEIN SYNTHESIS

We have now come to the heart of the matter and we must consider how proteins are made. As proteins are perhaps the most essential and typical of all the constituents of living cells, this is clearly one of the basic questions about life, which has attracted an enormous amount of attention in recent years.

As we have seen, the proteins are highly complex chains of amino acids arranged in a particular order. There are about twenty separate amino acids and we know that there must be in the cell a mechanism which reproduces exactly and without error the specific order of the amino acids in every natural protein. The number of possible ways of arranging say a chain of one hundred units chosen from twenty different kinds is enormous. The cell selects the amino acids and places them in the correct order with great ease and speed. In many bacteria a new generation is produced in thirty minutes or even less time. In this period, the full complement of proteins for a new cell must be synthesized. It is evident that the protein synthesizing mechanism works with great speed and efficiency. What is its nature?

In the first instance we need to know something of the nature of microsomes and other cytoplasmic constituents. It has been found that the cytoplasmic constituents, as well as the nucleus, contain a nucleic acid component known as ribonucleic acid (RNA), which is somewhat similar to the DNA of the nucleus, but differs from it in using a different sugar and also one of the component bases is different.

Nucleic acids of this type are probably present in most of the cytoplasmic constituents, and occur to a marked extent in the microsomes; but they are present in a highly concentrated form in the sub-microsomes, which were mentioned above. As the initial site of protein synthesis appeared to be the microsomes and it was suspected that RNA was implicated, it was natural to consider the sub-microsomes as a possible site of the synthesizing mechanism. It has long been thought that the synthesis of a protein with amino acids in a particular order requires a 'template' which will act as a guide or determiner of the order of the amino acids and it was therefore suggested that the RNA provides a template to guide protein synthesis. The great difficulty was to see how it could function in such a way.

Very recently suggestions have been made which may offer the solution of this puzzle. It appears that the synthesis of protein occurs in two stages. It has been shown by Lippman that in the first stage the amino acids are 'activated' by combination with the high energy phosphate compounds, which, as was mentioned above, are the final products of the oxidation of sugars. It has also been found that, for each amino acid there is in the cell a specific enzyme which can activate it and it alone and this enzyme enables it to be combined with some of the component parts of the nucleic acid (RNA) present in the microsomes.

A very interesting suggestion as to how the specificity is brought about has been made by Drs Crick, Orgel and Griffiths, of Cambridge University.

It has long been thought that the order of the bases in nucleic acid provided a 'code' which is stored up in the DNA of the chromosomes and transmitted to give rise to the actual templates on which the proteins are formed. The great difficulty was to see how such a code could be constructed making use only of the four different bases which are present in the nucleic acids. With these bases there can only be four different ways of filling one place of the nucleic acid threads, so that a code based on single places can only give four different signals and this is not enough to indicate the order in structures of twenty amino acids. However, if we can allow two places in the nucleic acid thread for each signal, we can fill them in sixteen different ways and if we allow three places in the nucleotide thread for a signal, we can have sixty-four different combinations, because there are sixty-four different ways in which four kinds of units can be arranged in groups of three.

The minimum signal which has enough possibilities to cope with about twenty amino acids is therefore one which uses three places in the nucleic acid thread as a code for the placing of a single amino acid. However, if we were to adopt some such code as this, we should need some way of distinguishing the three places which constitute a signal from adjacent places. So far as we know in a nucleic acid thread, all the places are equivalent to each other and there is no way in which one group of three are distinguished from another group of three. For example, if the four bases are represented by A, B, C and D, we might have the series:

ABCCADBCACDBAC

If groups of three are to constitute a signal, how are we to distinguish one group of three from others? We need to know where the groups of three which belong to the code start. Thus, in the example given above, the signal might be given either by ABC or the adjacent BCA or CCA. It would be impossible to make use of both ABC and BCA as signals for separate amino acids, as they overlap.

Crick, Orgel and Griffiths have offered a solution of this difficulty. They pointed out that out of the sixty-four possible combinations of A, B, C and D taken three at a time, it is possible to pick out twenty which are distinctive in the sense that they will not overlap with any others. They suggest that these twenty combinations are the ones which Nature uses as code signals for the twenty amino acids of which, with few exceptions, proteins are made up.

The whole picture of protein synthesis which is beginning to emerge is thus a very complex one.[1] The genes or hereditary particles are composed of the DNA of the cell nucleus and these carry the code for the synthesis of the specific proteins of the cell. But the code is not expressed directly. In the first place it is transferred to the RNA of the cell particles. How this is done is not clearly known, as the process has never been actually demonstrated. But we must suppose that the two complementary strands of DNA are separated and a complementary strand which is composed of RNA is built up on similar principles on one of them. This RNA enters the microsomal granules where it forms a 'template' for the construction of protein molecules on the lines discussed above. Here the code functions by determining the order of the amino acids in the way I have already mentioned. That is, each amino acid is 'activated' by a specific enzyme which attaches to it the 'nucleotide' groups, which are going to enable it to find its place by means of the code signal. Thus, suppose that the code on the RNA for a particular amino acid X is ABC. X is attached by its enzyme, not to ABC itself, but to the exact complement of ABC which we shall call A'B'C'. This grouping can only combine with its complement ABC on the RNA template and thus the position of X in the peptide chain is fixed by the position of ABC in the nucleic acid template (Fig. 13). Similarly the amino acids Y and Z find their positions by being combined with the code group which we may suppose to be A'B'D' and B'B'A'. The next step is the combination of X with its neighbours Y and Z. This will liberate the code groups A'B'C', etc. which are free to act again in the same way.

It should be made clear that this proposed mechanism has not been completely established—many parts of it have not yet been found experimentally. In fact, all we have are a series of hints. But important experiments carried out by Dr Zamecnik and his collaborators

[1] Readers who do not want to go into details can omit this and turn to p. 54.

at Boston have isolated some parts of the process. They have shown that the amino acids are first attached to small unidentified nucleotide fragments by the agency of enzymes in the cell sap. From this state they have shown that transfer to the microsomal granules can take place.

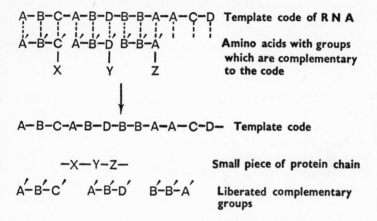

FIG. 13. How the code carried by the RNA template might operate. Each amino acid is attached to the complementary code grouping which enables it to find its place in the sequence

These experiments appear to provide the beginning of a solution of one of the greatest mysteries of life—how specific proteins are made. The mechanism suggested is extremely complicated and we can only guess as to how it was established to begin with, but it is clear that nothing less complicated would be able to explain the appearance in the cell of such a host of highly individual proteins.

VI

Genes and Mutations

꒳

We have already seen that there is much evidence that the genes, which carry the unit hereditary characters from one generation to another, are located in the chromosomes and as the chromosomes are composed of nucleic acid (DNA) and proteins, it was believed that DNA must be at least an important constituent of the gene. The first concrete evidence in support of this view was the discovery of 'transforming principles' which consist entirely of DNA. The initial observation which led to the discovery of these factors was made by Griffith. The bacterium, *Pneumococcus,* occurs in two forms, one of which is covered by a capsule of starchy material and the other is bare. Griffith found that when live 'bare' bacteria were injected into mice together with dead bacteria of the encapsulated type, the former acquired the ability to grow a capsule and this ability, when once acquired, was transmitted to succeeding generations. In other words, the bare variety which had gone through numerous generations without any change, acquired the ability, when treated with non-living material, to grow a capsule of its own. Later it was found by Dawson and Sia that it was not necessary to grow the bacteria in an animal. The same transformation could be brought about in the same way in a test tube.

Alloway showed that the whole of the dead encapsulated bacterium was not necessary, but extracts from it were effective. Finally, in 1944, three American workers, Avery, McCleod and McCarty, isolated the active agent or transforming principle and showed that it had all the properties of a nucleic acid (DNA). Similar observations have since been made with a considerable number of other bacteria which exist in two well-defined forms. The transformation from one form to another can be effected by material, which in every case has turned out to be DNA. Once transformed the bacteria continue to reproduce in the transformed state, so that their genetic constitution must have been altered. It is concluded from this that the material added contains a *gene*, and the conclusion is inevitable that in these instances the gene is in fact a nucleic acid (DNA).

How the different types of one kind of bacteria arise in the first instance is not very clear. But it is known that if colonies of bacteria are kept, occasionally a change will occur in a bacterium which is transmitted to its progeny. Such a change, known as a *mutation*, is not a very infrequent phenomenon and is responsible for the many strains of bacteria which exist.

Mutations of this kind are probably responsible for the resistance to drugs which bacteria develop. For example, it is well known that common bacteria present in infections may develop a resistance to penicillin. This means that a change has occurred, with the development of a new strain which can multiply in the presence of penicillin, because it has a somewhat different constitution.

Hotchkiss, in 1951, made the surprising discovery that penicillin-sensitive strains of Pneumococcus can be transformed into penicillin-resistant strains simply by adding to the former DNA derived from the latter. In other words the property of being able to grow and multiply in the presence of penicillin is conferred by addition of DNA, and again, once acquired, this ability is transmitted to descendants. The same phenomenon has been found in other cases, e.g. the streptomycin-resistance which is developed by a certain type of influenza bacillus.

All these experiments supported the idea that DNA alone was capable of behaving as a *gene*. This demonstration in higher organisms is, of course, much more difficult because there is no way in which we can introduce extraneous DNA into the germ cells of animals. It would certainly be fascinating if it were possible to remove one chromosome and replace it by another with a different hereditary background, or if it were possible to change the characteristics of an animal by introducing DNA from another species. The difficulty is to get the DNA into appropriate cells and as we shall see later animals reject nucleoproteins even from other individuals of their own kind. If this were not so it might be possible to make all sorts of composite animals. It has been reported recently by J. Benoit, P. Leroy and C. and R. Vendrely that the injection of DNA made from ducks of one variety (Khaki Campbells) into ducks of a second variety (Pekin) from the eighth day after hatching, caused definite changes in the latter. Usually the Khaki Campbells are large birds with yellow beaks and creamy-yellow plumage, while the Pekins are smaller ducks with greenish-black beaks. The beaks of the treated ducks developed bold black smudges against a background which was either yellow or rose pink. It was suggested that these modifications were also transmitted to the progeny; but further experiments are required before it can be regarded as certain that DNA injected into animals can really change the genetic characteristics.

The biological method of doing this experiment is to mate male and female organisms of the same species which have a different genetic constitution. As I have mentioned above, 'crossing over' of material derived from the two parents occurs and the progeny will carry different combinations of the genes available. From a study of these, it is possible to distinguish the genes of different individuals.

An enormous amount of work of this kind has been done with the fruit fly, or drosophila, which has been bred through many generations. These flies are very convenient. A new generation appears in about a week and they are simple to keep and to feed. If a large number of flies is studied, every now and then a spontaneous change or mutation occurs, which is transmitted to the progeny of this individual in accordance with the laws of genetics. In the course of many years of work by Morgan and his colleagues in Columbia University, no less than 800 distinct mutations were observed, which could be bred true to type and were undoubtedly due to distinct changes in the genes. The chromosomes of the flies were examined at the same time. This is easy to do because it happens that, in the larva state, the chromosomes of their salivary glands are enormously developed and can be seen even with a low power microscope (Plate 4) to have a banded structure. Changes in the chromosome corresponding to the different mutations can easily be seen, so that it is possible to identify a mutation with a particular part of the chromosome. In fact chromosome maps showing the positions of many genes have been worked out.

The essential characteristic of a gene is that it has a permanence which enables the same character to be transmitted through innumerable generations. But at the same time new characters sometimes appear (or old characters disappear). It has been estimated that in the fruit fly, on the average, an individual gene may undergo a mutation in something like a million generations. This means that no mistake is made in the copying of the original gene until on the average correct reproduction has occurred a million times—which would occupy, with the fruit fly, between a thousand and ten thousand years. Professor J. B. S. Haldane has calculated that with human genes the likelihood of a mutation may be only of the order of once in a million years. Nevertheless the fact that such changes in the genic material can occur is of great importance because without it evolution could not take place. The majority of gene changes will be disadvantageous and will cause the death of the organism or their non-survival. But very occasionally valuable mutations may occur somewhere in the population of a species and the sexual process ensures that the new gene will be combined with the others present. In fact, sexual combination of genes, together with natural selection eventually leads to the combination of all the best genes in the species.

According to this view, evolution is the result of two qualities of the genic substance; it has to be permanent and pass on the same characteristic through many generations. Some species, e.g. the primitive coelacanth fish *Latimeria chalumnae,* have remained essentially unchanged since the tertiary times. If it were not so, a species would not continue to exist and exhibit recognizable characters. But the ability to change must also be present or evolution would not occur at all.

Effects of X-rays and Atomic Radiations on Living Cells

The great permanence of the gene shows that the material it is made of must be well shielded from external influences, and at one time it was thought that the genes were so well protected that they could not be modified by any external agency applied to the organism.

However, it was discovered by H. J. Müller in 1928 that the frequency with which gene mutations occurred could be definitely increased by exposing the germ cells to X-rays and similar penetrating radiations, which are produced by radioactive substances. The characteristic property of all these radiations is their ability to penetrate into tissue and produce chemical changes within it. The dangerous nature of X-rays was discovered very early by the pioneer workers, who often suffered serious and frequently fatal X-ray burns. The widespread use of radioactive substances and, even more, the possible exposure of large populations to the effects of radiations from atomic bombs, has greatly increased the importance and interest of these effects and in recent years an enormous amount of scientific research has been devoted to them.

The radiations concerned are called ionizing radiations because they are sufficiently powerful to disrupt the molecules of matter through which they pass, with the formation of electrically charged fragments or ions. They usually bring this about by knocking one or more electrons out of the neutral molecules they pass through. The intensity of the radiation is measured by the number of ions primarily formed in the material through which the radiation passes. It is expressed in terms of a unit, the *roentgen,* which is the quantity of radiation which brings about 10^{12} (a million million) ionizations in a cubic centimetre of the substance. This may seem to be a very large number, but it is small compared with the number of molecules present in the same volume. For example, one cubic centimetre of water contains roughly 3×10^{22} water molecules,[1] so that one roentgen (1 r) ionizes only one water molecule in every 3×10^{10} (i.e. 30,000 million). The primary ions formed have a very short life and change into reactive substances called radicals (often H or OH in water) which are capable of producing chemical changes in other molecules present.

There is no doubt that all ionizing radiations have a very damaging effect on all living cells. In the case of a rat the average lethal dose is about 700 roentgens. The lethal dose for a human being is probably less, not more than 400-500 roentgens over the whole body. We can easily calculate how many ionizations a typical rat cell receives with this lethal dose. The volume of a typical cell (taken as a sphere about 10^{-3} cms. across) will be about 5×10^{-10} cubic centimetres (i.e. about 2,000 million to 1 cubic centimetre). From this it follows that the lethal dose, *viz.* 700 roentgens, will give rise to 350,000 ionizations[2] in every typical cell. This may seem to be quite a large number, but it is small compared with the total number of protein molecules present in such a cell.

Careful studies have shown that only a small proportion of the protein molecules in the cell are damaged by a lethal dose. The reason for the death of the animal in such cases is still unknown—it may be that there are cell constituents which are both essential to the life of the cell and are also damaged by very small doses of radiation, but they have not been identified with certainty. Some organs in the body, such as lymphatic glands, are more sensitive to radiation than others. The bone marrow, in which the red blood corpuscles are made, is particularly sensitive.

It has been found possible by adding certain protective substances like cysteine or cystamine to increase the lethal dose of radiation, i.e. the animal will tolerate a greater dose and still recover. However, these substances have to be present in the body before exposure to the radiation—addition after the exposure has very little effect.

The bone marrow of animals has the very important function of being the source of the red blood corpuscles. It is also a highly sensitive organ and an important effect of radiation has been to decrease the power which the animal has of replacing its red blood corpuscles. Dr Jacobson of Chicago discovered that, if bone marrow from an unexposed animal is injected into the exposed animal, it helps it to recover from the effects of radiation. It is also possible to use bone marrow from another species to some extent. For example, bone marrow from mice will help an irradiated rat to recover. It does this by taking the place temporarily of the damaged bone marrow mech-

[1] This means 3 followed by 22 noughts.
[2] $700 \times 5 \times 10^{-10} \times 10^{12} = 350,000$.

anism and keeping the rat going until its own bone marrow is functioning again.

Another important finding, made by the workers in the atomic research laboratory at Oak Ridge, Tennessee, and also in Germany, that although animals which have received less than the lethal dose of radiation recover, their average life is shortened. A shortening of life is caused by even small doses of radiation. With rats, the shortening of the average life is approximately 0·61 days for each roentgen received. This is an important phenomenon, the meaning and cause of which are rather obscure at present. It is very remarkable that a similar shortening of life of the offspring occurs if the spermatozoa of the father are exposed to the radiation! It follows that factors which determine the length of life are carried by the spermatozoa.

Very little information is available about the actual effects of exposure to radiations on the life span of human beings; but it has been observed in the United States that, while the average life of physicians having no known contact with radiation is 65·7 years, that of radiologists, who may be exposed to radiations in the course of their work, is only 60·5 years. The average exposure in these cases is unknown.

Another serious effect of ionizing radiations, which may be mentioned briefly here, is that they give rise in some cases to malignant growths (cancers). Many miners in the mines of Joachimsthal, in which radioactive minerals are extensively worked, die of cancer of the lung, probably due to inhaling radioactive gases such as radon and also radioactive dust particles. Workers with radioactive paints, used for producing luminous watch dials, etc, are liable to contract various diseases, one of which is cancer of bones. Radium, which is used in these paints, is similar to calcium in its properties and finds its way into the bones and may remain there for many years. A correlation has been found between the incidence of bone cancer in these cases and the amount of radium present in the bones. It has been estimated that 0·1 microcurie of radium in the bones of an individual gives a probability of 0·5 per cent of a bone sarcoma occurring (*Bull. Atomic Scientists,* June 1957).

A similar effect has become of importance in connection with the explosion of atomic bombs. One of the products of the explosion is radioactive strontium which has a long life and may find its way into bones. Radioactive strontium is disseminated through the upper atmosphere following an explosion and is slowly carried to the surface of the earth in rain. It is taken up by plants from rain water and, when the plants are eaten by animals, a part (5 per cent) is retained in the animal. In this way, at two or three removes, human beings acquire strontium originating in atomic bomb explosions. The retention is greater in the growing bones of young people than of older people. However at the present time the effect is not serious as the amount of strontium present in the bones of human beings has reached about a thousandth of a microcurie and one microcurie is regarded as a reasonably safe permissible amount. However, even this small amount is expected to produce a certain incidence of bone cancer.

Another well-established effect of radiation is a disease of the bone marrow known as leukemia. This is a kind of cancer in which an uncontrolled excessive formation of white blood cells occurs. Many cases of leukemia have occurred among the survivors of the atomic bomb at Hiroshima and the observations recorded in the following Table show that there is a definite correlation between the incidence of the disease and the amount of radiation received:

Distance from explosion	Incidence of leukemia between January 1947—August 1955 (per 10,000 persons)
more than 2,000 metres	2
1,500 — 2,000 metres	3-4
1,000 — 1,500 metres	28
below 1,000 metres	128

The possible effect of ionizing radiations from radioactive substances on the genic material is of even greater moment than the effect on the health and life of the individual. As we have seen, ionizing radiations are capable of giving rise to mutations and it has been found that a great majority of the mutations are deleterious, i.e. result in the loss of a useful character.

It must be remembered that such mutations may remain concealed for several generations. This is because all the body cells contain two chromosomes, one from each parent. Thus, if one of the chromosomes is complete, the fact that the other is damaged may be hidden and only come to light when two individuals with the same mutated gene produce offspring.

It has been of great importance to make an estimate of the frequency with which mutations are likely to occur as a result of exposure to ionizing radiations. The first estimate of this kind was made by H. J. Müller, working with fruit flies, who found that the exposure of the spermatozoa of the fruit fly to only one roentgen of X-rays increased the mutation frequency (for certain mutations) no less than ten times. W. L. Russell, at Oak Ridge, has made studies on mice exposed to ionizing radiation and found an effect at least ten times that observed with fruit flies. However, the natural mutation frequency is very low, so that it is better to express the result directly in terms of the number of mutations observed in the whole population. It was found that the average frequency of a particular kind of mutation was of the order of 25×10^{-8} per roentgen. This means that if one hundred million mice received one roentgen each, twenty-five mutations of this particular type would occur. The figure for the fruit fly is about one tenth as much.

We can apply this figure to human beings on the assumption that the human mutation rate is the same as that of mice. Many of the survivors of Hiroshima must have received 200 roentgens of radiation. The chance of mutation of one particular gene in one of these individuals may thus be expected to be about $200 \times 25 \times 10^{-8}$, i.e. $5,000 \times 10^{-8}$ or 0·5 in 10,000. As each individual probably has at least 10,000 genes in all, which are equally liable to be affected, it follows that there is a high probability that each individual who survived Hiroshima and received 200 roentgens of radiation carries at least one mutated gene of one kind or another in the chromosomes of each of his germ cells.

We can now ask how ionizing radiations bring about mutations. It is easy to observe that exposure to these radiations has a marked effect on chromosomes. When the chromosomes of cells are examined under the microscope after exposure to radiations, visible effects are frequently found, such as breakage of a chromosome into two portions (Plate 9). This is sometimes followed by more complex happenings. If two chromosomes are broken, the two sets of broken ends may join up with the wrong partners. When replication of the chromosomes occurs, it often happens that the two new daughter chromosomes do not separate from each other completely, but a 'bridge' forms between them which continues to hold them together. Such effects are observed in a proportion of the cells, even after fairly small doses of radiations. With plant material, Swanson observed at least one chromosome aberration per cell with 150 roentgens of radiation.

An important feature of the genetic damage due to radiations is that it is cumulative. It is believed that the effect is the same whether a dose is delivered all at one time or in very small quantities over a considerable period. It follows that exposure to very weak sources of radiation for a long period may be as important as a large intensity for a short time.

It is therefore of great interest to estimate the prospects of genetic damage to human beings from natural and other sources of radiation. We are in fact all the time exposed to radiations from (1) cosmic rays; (2) radioactive gases or dust in the ground and atmosphere produced by natural sources. In addition, we may receive radiations from (3) artificial sources of radiations such as X-rays used for medical examinations and radioactive paints used on watch dials; (4) radioactivity derived from the 'fallout' from the explosion of atomic bombs and of thermonuclear weapons. A very careful study of these effects has been made by government committees in both the United Kingdom and in the United States of America.

It is estimated that from natural sources of radiation including cosmic rays and naturally occurring radioactive substances, an individual in the United Kingdom will receive a total dose in the reproductive organs of about three roentgens during a period of thirty years, which is taken as the average reproductive period. This appears to be less than the amount of exposure which would be required to double the natural spontaneous rate at which some mutations occur. The average dose received by the reproductive organs from the diagnostic use of X-rays is estimated to be about 20 per cent of the dose from natural sources. The dose of radiation which individuals are likely to receive from the radioactive 'fallout' from atomic or thermonuclear explosions is comparatively small and even if continued indefinitely at the same rate as during the last few years, would only amount to one per cent of the radiation from natural sources.

To find the actual chemical changes which are responsible for the biological effects of radiation much work has been done on the effects of the radiations on nucleic acids. It is only necessary to say here that the radiations do bring about numerous different kinds of chemical changes. They not only destroy the bases on which, as we have seen, the genetic properties ultimately depend; but they are also capable of breaking a DNA particle into two or more parts. There is little doubt that these chemical changes are sufficient to give rise to the observed effects of the radiations on the chromosome and consequently to the genetic effects which they produce.

If the genes can be damaged by chemical reactions which penetrating radiations bring about within the cell, should we not expect that chemical substances could be introduced, which would bring about similar effects? It used to be thought that anything which happened to the body could not affect the germinal cells, so well were they protected. However, following Müller's experiments with X-rays it was found by Dr C. Auerbach and Drs Robson and Carr in Edinburgh that mutations could be produced in the fruit fly by the application of certain chemicals. The chemical substances which they used as known as 'mustards', a reactive type of substance which was developed for use in chemical warfare. It was noticed that the wounds produced by 'mustard gas' were in some respects similar to

X-ray burns, and this suggested the possibility of these substances causing mutations.

Since the original experiments of Dr Auerbach and her colleagues, a great many substances have been discovered which are capable of producing mutations. They are not usually very highly reactive substances. One of the necessary features of such a substance will be its ability to reach the nucleus and react there with the chromosomal filaments. If it is too reactive it will react with the first proteins and other substances it meets when it enters the cell. One property of the chemical mutagens, as they are called, is their ability to deliver a delayed punch in the cell nucleus. But some of the mutagens are apparently only very weakly reactive (e.g. certain hydrocarbons) and the nature of their action is still unknown. But they have one feature which is shared by all or nearly all of them; they are also 'carcinogenic' agents—they are capable of causing some types of cancer (see p. 95).

They cause changes in the chromosomes which are very similar to those produced by ionizing radiations. Not only are chromosome breaks observed; but a 'stickiness' similar to that caused by X-rays, i.e. in cell division the two sets of chromosomes do not pull away from each other cleanly but leaves 'bridges' of chromosome material between them. In fact it appears that the two sets of chromosomes are joined together at one or more places. It is significant that many of the substances which give rise to these effects are known as 'cross-linking' agents, i.e. they can join two protein molecules together. It is likely that they do join in this way the two dividing strands of the chromosome fibre.

STUDYING MUTATIONS WITH MICRO-ORGANISMS

Many genetic experiments have also been carried out with micro-organisms—fungi or bacteria. Work with these organisms has the great advantage that the time taken to pass through one generation is very short so that very large numbers of individuals can be dealt with, and it is possible to make a thorough analysis of the frequency of mutations and mutations which only occur very infrequently can be discovered.

A favourite material for experiments of this kind is the fungus *Neurospora*. Beadle and Tatum exposed the spores of this fungus to X-rays. Many of them are killed by this treatment, but among those which survive mutants are found. These have lost the ability to perform one or more of the chemical reactions which the original 'wild type' neurospora could perform.

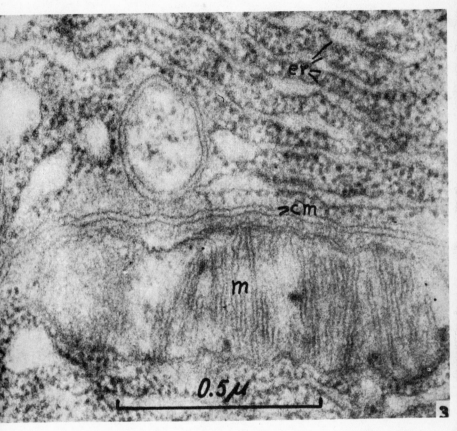

7   Fine structure in the cell interior. Electron micrograph of a cell from the pancreas, showing sub-microsomes (small round bodies attached to the microsomal membranes). The large sausage-shaped object is a mitochondrion. (From Sjöstrand and Hanson, *Exp. Cell Research*, 7, 393, 1954)

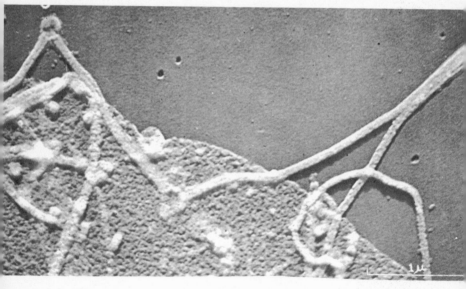

8   Electron micrographs of Influenza A virus adhering to a red fowl cell. The upper photograph shows the round virus particles and the lower photograph the long filaments they sometimes form adhering to the edge of the cell. Photographs by Drs Chu, Dawson and Elford

The original 'wild' neurospora is an organism with remarkable synthetic ability. All it requires to live and to grow, besides water and some inorganic elements, are glucose or some other source of carbon, ammonia and the vitamin *biotin*. Out of these simple materials it makes everything it requires. It makes twenty amino acids, a variety of purines or pyrimidines, nucleic acids and proteins, aneurin, riboflavin, pyridoxin, pantothenic acid, folic acid, choline, inositol, and no doubt numerous other substances.

The mutants produced by X-rays often lack the ability to make one or other of these compounds and growth will not take place unless the necessary compound is supplied. It is thus quite easy to isolate a mutant which lacks the ability to make one compound (see

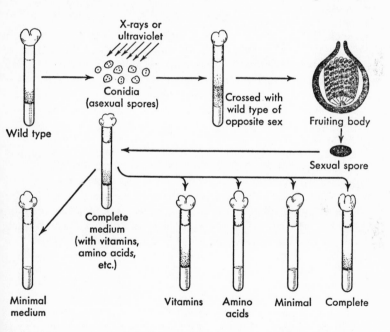

FIG. 14. How mutants of the fungus, *Neurospora,* are made and tested for their nutritional requirements. Spores of the 'wild type' of the fungus are exposed to X-rays or ultra-violet light. They are then 'crossed' with spores of the original wild type and the progeny is examined (this ensures that the changes observed are genuine effects on the genes or mutations). The spores so obtained are tested for their ability to grow in various solutions. In the first place those which cannot grow in a minimal medium which supports the wild type, but can grow when a complete set of supplements (vitamins, amino acids, etc.) are isolated. Separate tests are then made to discover which of the supplementary substances they require

E

Fig. 14) and then to grow it in the presence of this compound. Quite a large number of such mutants have been produced, all of which lack the enzyme which is required to make the missing substance.

It is inferred from this that in each case one gene has been damaged by X-rays and this gene controls the formation of one enzyme. Occasionally strains of the fungus are produced where two or more substances must be added to the basal medium to enable them to grow. But it can be shown by cross-breeding experiments that the genes are distinct and it is only a matter of chance that two have been damaged in the same spore. A gene that has been lost can be replaced by cross-breeding with a strain which possesses it. This is the clearest evidence we have for a close, and probably a one-to-one, relation between genes and enzymes. According to this the gene essentially contains the pattern which guides the formation of the enzyme. It is probable that it carries this pattern as a sequence of bases in DNA, as described in Chapter V. If this is so, it is evident that damage to the pattern of bases in DNA will clearly interfere with the ability of this material to pass on its message. The damage might be only damage to the bases at one or two critical points which would interfere with the code; or it might be a break of the DNA thread which would prevent an intact protein being formed. Many of the stages by which genes bring about their effects still remain to be worked out. It has been sometimes possible in micro-organisms to track down the whole chain of reactions by which a particular chemical substance is formed, in a number of stages, each of which require a special enzyme. It is found that each step is controlled by a separate gene. If this gene is damaged by X-rays, the progeny of this individual is unable to perform the corresponding process, so that the whole sequence of reactions is broken at this point. If the substance which the organism is now unable to make is added artificially, growth will proceed normally; but otherwise the substance which is formed as an intermediate, just before the break in the sequence, accumulates because the organism is unable to make use of it. By experiments of this kind, many complex sequences of reactions have been worked out.

Another example of the control of protein synthesis by genes has been found in connection with 'sickle cell anaemia', a human disease which is inherited according to the Mendelean rules and is therefore under genic control. It has been found by V. M. Ingram that the haemoglobin extracted from sickle cells differs from normal human haemoglobin in a single amino acid only out of the 300 present in the molecule—one glutamic acid group in the normal haemoglobin being replaced by valine.

[1] *Nature* **180**, 326, 1957.

VIII

Viruses—Cell Parasites

꿈

A good many years ago it was discovered that there are agents of disease which are much smaller than bacteria, since they pass through filters that retain bacteria and also cannot be seen under the microscope. As long ago as 1892, Ivanowski observed that the sap of tobacco plants which were infected with tobacco mosaic disease still had the power of infecting healthy plants, when rubbed on their leaves, even after it had been passed through a fine porcelain filter. In 1898, Loeffler and Frosch showed that the infective agent of foot and mouth disease of cattle could also pass through such filters.

The importance of these observations was not at first understood, but gradually a distinction was drawn between bacteria, which were usually visible under the microscope and were stopped by fine filters, and filter-passing agents which were submicroscopic and were called viruses.

The list of virus diseases, even of man, is now very long and includes measles, mumps, influenza, poliomyelitis, chickenpox, rabies and yellow fever.

For many years viruses remained in the realm of the invisible. Estimates of their size were made by various means. For example, Dr W. J. Elford made collodion membranes having pores of different sizes and was able to estimate the sizes of the different agents by their ability to pass through the pores. It was found that, although submicroscopic, they were much larger than most protein molecules (see Fig. 15).

Methods of concentrating and purifying the virus material were also worked out. Dr W. M. Stanley, in 1935, applied to infected tobacco plant juice the methods of salt precipitation which had been successfully applied to the separation of the enzymes. He obtained a protein of high molecular weight, which was highly infective and could be prepared in a semi-crystalline condition. Here was a pure, or comparatively pure chemical substance, which had the ability of infecting healthy plants. When introduced into the plant, an extremely small quantity infects the plant with the disease and it also multiplies extensively so that, after a time, a much larger quantity of infective material than that introduced can be obtained from the plant cells. It therefore appeared that this substance had one of the characteristic features of life, *viz.*, the ability to multiply in an appropriate environment.

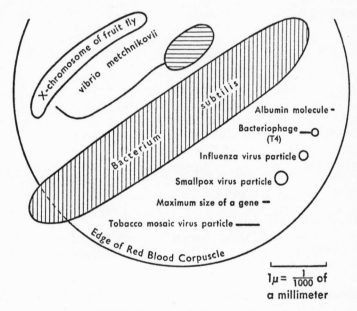

FIG. 15. Relative sizes of viruses and bacteria

A considerable number of viruses has now been isolated in what appears to be a pure condition, some of them in a crystalline state. Crystallinity simply means that the particles all have the same well-defined regular shape so that they will pack together in a lattice arrangement, forming crystals which have regular geometrical shapes. More recently many viruses have been photographed under the electron microscope and their shapes and sizes made visible (see Plates 8 and 10). It is found that they vary greatly in size and shape. Some are spheres; others, like the tobacco mosaic virus, are cylindrical rods; others resemble a tadpole with a tail. The spherical ones easily pack into a crystalline form, and the long cylinders line up in one direction.

It was shown by Pirie that they are not simple proteins, but nucleo-proteins, i.e. compounds of a nucleic acid with proteins. The nucleic acid is sometimes similar to the DNA of the chromosomes (but the bases present are sometimes different, e.g. T2 bacteriophage contains hydroxymethylcytosine instead of the usual cytosine); in others the nucleic acid is similar to that present in the cytoplasm (RNA). Plant viruses frequently contain RNA and many animal viruses DNA.

The infectivity is usually highly specific in that a strain of the virus will only live and multiply in one particular host species, e.g. tobacco mosaic virus only attacks tobacco plants, and the common polio-myelitis virus attacks very few animal species. Sometimes the virus can multiply only in some strains of a species and not in others, e.g. some varieties of potato such as the King Edward are resistant to potato mosaic virus. They cannot usually be made to multiply in an 'artificial' medium, although some will grown when introduced into living eggs. Either their nutritional requirements are so exacting that proper mixtures which will support them have not yet been found, or they require to make use of the whole apparatus for providing energy and growth substances, which is present in living cells.

Are we to class these substances as living or non-living? They have the basic properties of living things—the ability to reproduce them-selves in a suitable environment. But the size and crystallizability of their molecules brings them close to the inanimate world. They seem to be on the dividing line between the two worlds. Dr Stanley has said: 'As we go from the admittedly non-living to the admittedly living, I think there must be a transition stage where there are entities that may possess some properties of the non-living and of living things. What could fill this place more simply and logically than the high molecular weight virus proteins that are intermediate in com-plexity betwen the protein enzymes and hormones, the wonderful properties of which we already recognize, and the system of proteins that we call protoplasm and which constitutes life? There is evidence that even within the virus group there is a gradual increase of com-plexity of structure from the small nucleo-proteins to the more "elementary-body" type of virus.[1] There is, however, no sharp break. . . .'

It seems that a certain degree of complexity is needed before an organism can maintain itself as an independent living thing with the ability to live on its environment and grow and multiply. As we have seen, this ability involves a most complicated apparatus of reactions which will extract raw materials and energy sources from the food and use them not only to maintain life but to make all the enzymes

[1] Large round virus particles, about 175 mμ across.

and proteins required. The virus particles do not have this ability, but they can make use of the apparatus which is provided by their host cells. They must therefore be regarded as parasites and, like parasitic animals, they are intimately related to their host species.

It is possible that the virus particles have arisen as a mutation of a normal self-reproducing constituent of the cells in which they grow. Suppose that a self-reproducing particle in a cell makes an error of reproduction and produces particles which, although they can 'live' and multiply in the cell, do not function correctly. They will be 'rogue' particles which interfere to a greater or less degree with the normal working of the cells. If they are introduced into healthy cells, they will continue to reproduce themselves there. But if they go on multiplying, they may cause such disturbances of the normal working of the cells that the organism eventually dies. This might mean the destruction of the virus as well, but the natural viruses have often developed efficient means of transferring themselves from infected to fresh organisms. They make use of all sorts of agents such as insects and birds to help them to disperse themselves. This implies a long period of adaptation.

The common viruses must have gone through innumerable generations since they first originated. They are in fact very variable. Even in short periods of observation, changes in their behaviour are often noticed and new strains appear. In fact, their successful maintenance may depend on this ability to change and so keep one step ahead of defensive mechanisms which the hosts may also develop.

Not only large organisms but also bacteria have their virus enemies. It was noticed by Twort in 1915 that bacterial cultures sometimes cleared suddenly and the bacteria appeared to break up and dissolve. A few drops from this liquid added to another culture caused it to behave in the same way. Two years later d'Herelle made similar observations. The agent which destroyed the bacteria could not only be transferred from one culture to another, but its activity increased with each transfer. This phenomenon is now recognized as being due to bacterial viruses, which are known as bacteriophages. Their form has been definitely demonstrated by electron micrographs of the particles. A number of different types have been found which differ considerably in size and shape. Plates 11 and 12 show some of the fine pictures of Dr R. W. G. Wyckoff of successive stages of the attack of *Bacterium coli*. The 'phage particles are easily recognized by their tadpole-like shapes, with short rod-shaped tails. The attack begins when one or two of these particles attach themselves to a bacterium. The material inside the 'phage particle then passes through the wall and multiplies within the cell until, finally, the whole of the interior appears to be filled with new particles which escape through the disrupted cell membrane.

It has been found that only the nucleic acid of the bacteriophage passes into the bacterial cell, the protein sack in which it was contained remaining outside. (Hershey and Chase, 1952.)

Once inside the bacterium, a very extraordinary series of changes occurs. The bacteriophage takes over, as it were, the whole chemistry of the cell for its own purpose. The cell begins to synthesize substances to make new bacteriophage. In some cases this involves making compounds which were not even present in the normal cell; thus T2 bacteriophage contains the base hydroxymethylcytosine instead of cytosine which is normally present in cells.

With the bacteriophage called T2, it has been shown that, for the first seven minutes after the entry of the agent into the bacterium, little can be observed to happen. The bacteriophage material appears to 'dissolve' and for a short time cannot be detected in the cell. After nine minutes the synthesis of new bacteriophage particles begins and continues until about the thirteenth minute, when all the available material in the cells has been used up and an average of 130 new particles of bacteriophage are formed in each bacterium. The bacteriophage particle has succeeded in imposing its pattern on the cell substances and has used them for its own purposes.

In the case of tobacco mosaic virus, it has been found by Fraenkel-Conrat and by G. Schramm that, if the protein is stripped off the virus particle, the nucleic acid (RNA) is still capable of causing the disease. It is true that the infectivity of the nucleic acid is a good deal less than that of the intact virus, but it is possible that the RNA is damaged in the preparative processes.

This experiment shows that the nucleic acid alone is capable of causing the synthesis of the whole virus in the infected plant. However, it has not yet been possible to cause infection of bacteria by using the nucleic acids prepared from bacteriophages. The probable reason for this is that the nucleic acid by itself is unable to enter the bacteria. The *tail* of the bacteriophage has a 'tip' which attaches itself to the bacterium which is being attacked and the nucleic acid is then injected into the bacterium through the tube. This is itself a very remarkable process and it is not understood how the nucleic acid from the head of the bacteriophage is pushed through the narrow tube which constitutes the tail (Fig. 16). It has recently been found by Dean Fraser and others, however, that if the bacteriophage DNA is added to broken bacterial protoplasts (i.e. bacteria without a cell wall) synthesis of new bacteriophage particles occurs.

This shows that the nucleic acid (DNA) of bacteriophage is capable not only of reproducing itself but also of forming the proteins present in the complete bacteriophage particles.

The bacteriophages offer a very favourable opportunity for the study of the elementary processes of reproduction as there is no doubt that replication occurs within the bacterium. M. Delbrück and W. T. Bailey discovered that bacteriophage particles are made up of still smaller units. They found that two different related strains of bacteriophage can be crossed with each other so as to produce

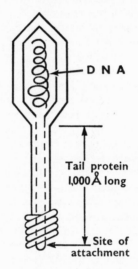

DNA

Tail protein
1,000 Å long

Site of
attachment

FIG. 16. A bacteriophage particle (slightly diagrammatic) (from E. A. Evans, *Texas Reports Biol. Medicine,* 15, 783 [1957])

a kind of hybrid. For example, one strain of virus known as T2 produces a small colony and can destroy a strain of the bacterium called A; while another strain known as T4r produces a large colony and can destroy a mutant strain called C. When both types are added together to a culture, not only are both of these original types released when the bacteria burst, but also two intermediate types, in which the characteristics are combined in a different way. One produces a large colony and destroys bacterium A. The other produces a small colony and destroys bacterium C. It appears that the characteristics of T2 and T4r have got mixed up in the new types, each of which has features drawn from both of the two parent types. The inference to be drawn from this is that bacteriophages break up in the cell into smaller particles which multiply independently and reassemble so as to give rise to all their possible combinations in the new individuals. Thus we find a kind of sexual reproduction even below the level of cells.

Another experiment by S. E. Luria of Indiana University also indicates the composite nature of bacteriophages. Viruses can be 'killed' by exposure to ultra-violet light. When infected by a single 'killed' bacteriophage particle the bacterium usually dies, but no multiplication of the virus takes place; but if two or more of the 'killed' virus particles enter the bacterium, it was found that they often multiplied as well as the undamaged virus. It looks as if the two damaged particles can share their parts and make up one complete individual between them. Luria estimated from his results that the 'phage particle has at least twenty independent units. When only one of these is damaged by ultra-violet light, the particle is incapable of multiplication, but the damaged unit can be made good from other particles.

This reconstitution of bacteriophages from damaged parents has been carried very much further by S. Benzer. By treatment with ultra-violet light or by ionizing radiations, it is possible to obtain a considerable number of mutants of a bacteriophage, which can be detected by their effects on their original host cell; or on slightly different strains of the bacterium, which react in different ways to infection. It is possible also to study the recombination of these different forms so as to reconstitute the original bacteriophage.

In these experiments it has been possible to construct a 'map' showing the order in which the different genes occur. This must mean that although recombination of the genes derived from two different 'phages can occur, it cannot be a haphazard process. That is, we must not think of the bacteriophage being dissolved into its component units which are then reassembled in a haphazard way. Although recombination of the parts occurs, it must be carried out in such a way that the order in which the genes are arranged is not lost. We must picture the bacteriophage particles as exchanging parts with each other, without losing their overall structure. This is similar to what happens in chromosomes, where as we have seen, in the formation of the germ cells, two chromosomes line up near each other and exchange. But the bacteriophage particle is much smaller than the chromosome and in fact it has been found that forty per cent of the DNA inside it is a single DNA particle, having a molecular weight probably of about fifteen million. The fact that exchange of genes between two bacteriophages can occur, means that a single

DNA molecule can exchange parts with another one, during the course of the duplication process. Of course this may not be a simple exchange of parts. It is quite likely that it occurs during the duplication of the nucleotide threads, in that the replication process which is forming a new nucleic acid particle along one fibre, jumps to a second one which happens to be in the vicinity.

Another remarkable discovery is that bacteria can exchange material carrying genic characteristics with each other. Plate 10, by E. L. Wollman, F. Jacob, and W. Hayes of the Pasteur Institute, Paris, shows two bacteria in conjunction. This is a kind of primitive sexual process. A bridge is formed between the bacteria, through which genic particles are exchanged. It has even been found possible to control the number of genes which are transferred by stopping the conjunction (by agitation) after different times. But this conjunction is a rare process affecting not more than one cell in a million—often even less —at any one time.

IX

A Community of Cells

By and large, all living cells have underlying mechanisms which are basically similar; they are all variations of the same theme. Thus to some extent the activities we have described so far are possessed by every living cell but, of course, some features are emphasized in some forms of life and repressed in others. The cells of unicellular organisms, like many bacteria, carry out all the functions of living by themselves. But in organisms consisting of many cells, there is usually specialization—some cells perform one function, some another. The organism becomes a society or community of cells in which each cell has a trade of its own. So we must now consider the life of the cell as a member of a community.

The first thing to note is that most of the organisms we are familar with contain very large numbers of cells. Even a small fly contains many millions of cells of many kinds. So however specialization started, it has obviously gone very far and we are not likely to learn much about how it came about from highly developed plants and animals.

The animal organism is particularly complex. There are cells set aside for the manufacture of special enzymes. In a mammal, the pancreas produces the digestive enzymes required in the intestine. The liver accumulates starch and also breaks it down to sugar. It also manufactures the main proteins of the blood serum. The red blood corpsucles are highly specialized structures for carrying oxygen and for regulating the carbon dioxide content of the blood.

So we have to ask how all these highly specialized cells come into existence. It is obvious that different forms of life have very different abilities to reproduce specialized structures. As a rule a plant is able to reproduce the whole plant from a small part of it. If you break off part of the stem of a growing plant and put it in the ground, it will often develop into a complete plant with roots and the ability to form flowers and seeds. The whole of the hereditary character of the plant is thus contained in every part of it—or at least in many of the parts.

This ability is much less developed in animals and the more highly developed the animal, the less is the power of reproducing lost parts. The higher animals like man only possess the power to a limited degree. If you cut your finger, the cells on either side of the cut will begin to multiply and spread over the wound, reproducing the main superficial features in doing so. In man, however, even the area of skin which can be replaced is rather limited; but animals often have a greater power of regenerating lost skin. Animals which are lower in the scale of life have much more extensive powers of regeneration. If a lizard loses its tail, it can grow a new one; so can a fish. A starfish will reproduce a ray which is broken off; some species of worms will grow a new individual from a small segment. In these cases the pattern of the whole individual is inherent in the parts and if the pattern is broken it is reformed.

These are very difficult facts to account for. Why are the cells of a mutilated starfish stimulated to growth and why does growth cease when it has just replaced the missing ray? We must ask how the pattern is carried in the organism.

The answer to these questions is not known. Indeed, little is known about how large organisms are formed, as they must be in all cases of sexual reproduction from a single fertilized egg cell, by successive divisions. Most of the higher organisms go back to a single fertilized egg cell at one stage of their life cycle, and the complex individual is formed by its successive divisions. About fifty successive divisions of the fertilized human ovum make a human being, with all the tissues of the human body, muscles, gut, liver, bone and brain. They are not merely made in sufficient quantities but precisely fashioned and exactly fitted together to make a functioning organism. It is obvious that, when cells in the growing embryo divide, they do not always give rise to two identical daughter cells. There must be many points at which *differentiation* occurs; the two daughter cells formed at one division will have different destinies; one may give rise to muscle and the other to nerve.

Very little is known about how this process of differentation occurs. It is certainly one of the darkest chapters of scientific knowledge—rather, one should say ignorance—at the present time. It would seem that, although in every cell division the chromosomes are replicated and one pair goes into each of the new daughter cells, yet there is a difference. One possibility is that the genes present in the chromosomes are covered, or inhibited, until they are required to carry out their function. This covering of the genes might be effected by the proteins present in the chromosome and it may be that after a certain number of subdivisions a gene becomes bare and therefore effective. But this is all very speculative and at the present time we can only be amazed at the precision with which the process of development occurs. Not only are cells produced which have distinct functions, but shape and form is accurately reproduced. The fingers grow at similar rates until the adult hand is formed. The characteristic features of the face are even passed down from one generation to another. We have to admit our almost complete ignorance of the controlling factors.

The ability of tissues to produce cells of differentiated types is greatest in the early stages of the development of the embryo and is lost as the completed organism takes shape. In fact, in the very early embryo, the future destiny of the cells seems to be largely undetermined. H. Spemann studied the early stages of development of the newt, before the stage known as gastrulation was reached. When the developing embryos were cut in two, a whole embryo developed from each half. However, this possibility is lost very quickly, and different parts are formed which have destinies (e.g. to form heart tissue, or intestine) which cannot be altered. Indeed these 'committed' cells are able to modify and impress their destiny on any other tissue implanted in them. It is necessary to suppose that effects of this kind are brought about by chemical substances, called organizers, but very little is known as to their nature. If we 'transplant a young and undifferentiated cell group into the region of the head,' says Paul Weiss,[1] 'it will form eye or brain; transplant it to the anterior trunk and it will form limb; or further back, kidney; and transplant it to the rear and it will form tail—the same cells forming different structures depending on the location. We may say: organizing factors take hold of the cells and direct them to appropriate functions.'

However, we know little about these organizing factors. Indeed, many biologists see more in an organism than a collection of cells. The cells all fit into each other and make a *whole*. If the whole is disrupted, it is reconstructed. 'Each cell develops in conformity with its surroundings. . . . It becomes a cone or a rod when in the retina, a cartilage cell when in the centre of the limb bud, a neurone when in the brain. Intrinsically capable of a variety of performances the cell receives some definite cue from the locality indicating which trend it is to follow. These cues are decidedly of supracellular origin.'

It follows from this that we must regard the organism as more than a mere collection of cells. It undoubtedly has a unity of its own, which in some ways impresses its character and needs on the individual

[1] *American Naturalist*, **24**, 43, 1946.

cells. How this unity or continuity is maintained is still unknown. Dr V. B. Wigglesworth put this point of view as follows:

'What is the nature of this continuity which the cells are at such pains to restore? May we not regard it as a chemical organism? On this view the difference of organization of unicellular and multi-cellular animals disappears. The latter, presumably for reasons of size, are subdivided into cellular units. But we may picture the organism as a chemical continium; a prodigious molecule . . . with active centres requiring specific hormones to enable them to exert their activity. . . . The cells do not "co-operate to mould the body form"—they merely carry and care for a small segment of the organism of which they are the servants.'

So we get glimpses of the organism as something more than a mere collection of cells; but we do not know what the additional factors or agents are. The whole organism is like a factory which is made up of many specialized workshops, each having a task of its own. Into each workshop or cell, raw materials come in and products are made and sent out. But the factory as a whole is more than a collection of work-shops; there must be planning and co-ordination which ensures that everything works at the right rate. There must be services, supplies, transport and flow sheets.

Little is known of these 'organizers'. Substances which promote growth have been isolated from plants and animals. Plant growth-promoting substances called auxins were isolated by Kögl and are of a comparatively simple nature. It was then found that quite simple synthetic substances which may not exist in plants, such as deriva-tives of indoleacetic and phenoxyacetic acids, also have this ability. They are now manufactured on a large scale and used as selective weed killers. This is because they cause dicotyledons to grow so rapidly that some phases of the growth process outstrip others and the plant dies. Another growth promoting substance is ghiberellic acid, which, when introduced in extraordinarily small amounts, causes dwarf varieties of plants, such as peas, to develop into giants. It does this by stimulating the growth of cells in the direction of the stem. The formation of flower-buds in plants is also controlled by chemical substances. In many cases the formation of the flower-bud is deter-mined by the length of the day, and not as we might think by the average temperature. The flower bud is often formed during the winter period and it has been found that a dark period of a certain length is necessary at the time when flower buds are formed. If this period is broken by a single flash of light, flowering may not occur. In this case the formation of the flower bud is stimulated by a sub-stance which accumulates in the dark. If the dark period is broken the active substance is removed by the sequence of 'light' reactions. Growth-promoting substances or hormones are also found in animals (see next Chapter).

This account of development may be concluded by mentioning the extraordinary transformations which insects, etc, undergo in their life cycles. The larva which hatches out from the egg may be an entirely different creature from the final insect, different in form, habits, food and construction. A butterfly or moth comes out of the egg as a gaily coloured caterpillar, which, as it eats and grows, sheds its hard skin several times. When it is fully grown, it winds itself into a cocoon and goes into a dormant state. Its tissues are dissolved and refashioned; and it ultimately emerges as an entirely different creature, the finished butterfly, which can lay eggs from which new larvae emerge. The genetic material carried by the chromosomes retains its integrity throughout these changes.

The moulting stages and the final metamorphosis into the adult insect have been carefully studied by Dr V. B. Wigglesworth in a blood-sucking bug, *Rhodnius prolixus*. This goes through five stages as a larva, with a moult between each, and then metamorphosis into the complete adult occurs. Between each moult it needs a single large meal of blood, and this starts off the train of events leading to the moulting, which takes place 12-15 days later. It has been shown that the moulting process is caused by a hormone, which is secreted into the blood by a gland situated in the brain.

It has also been found that the premature change into the adult is *prevented* by another hormone (the *juvenile* hormone) which is produced by the corpus allatum, a gland just behind the brain. If these glands are removed by chopping off the head of the larva at an appropriate interval after feeding, metamorphosis into the adult form takes place. On the other hand, if the head of a *young* larva is implanted into the fifth stage larva, which is on the point of turning into the adult insect, the metamorphosis is suppressed and a giant sixth stage larva is formed instead of an adult.

X

Chemical Messengers

As we have seen, a large community of cells must have controlling mechanisms, not only while the organism is growing but also to secure its harmonious functioning. The different kinds of cells must carry out their functions at the right time. A highly developed animal has of course very delicate mechanisms like nerves which help to control its actions, but it is probable that the earliest methods of control were chemical ones, such as are still found in simple organisms which have no nervous system. Although the nervous system is used for types of control in which speed is essential, nevertheless many of the chemical controls have been retained and are still made use of for many purposes, even in highly developed animals.

It has been known for many years that animals possess a variety of glands. Some have ducts leading into various organs, other are called ductless glands, because they release their secretions directly into the blood vessels. The importance of these glands began to be appreciated at the end of the nineteenth century, when it was found that the loss of one or more of them had serious effects on the behaviour of the body. Experiments were made on the effects of the removal of the glands of animals and it was found that the symptoms produced could be relieved by injecting extracts obtained from the glands of other animals. It was inferred from this that the glands produced chemical agents, which were called 'hormones' (chemical messengers) many of which have since been isolated. They differ greatly in chemical complexity. Some are quite simple substances, others are proteins. The study of hormones has become one of the largest and also one of the most successful branches of biochemistry. I shall not attempt to give an exhaustive description of these, but a few examples will illustrate their importance.

As long ago as 1884 it was recognized by Horsley that the removal or atrophy of the thyroid glands, a pair of small glands in the neck, produced cretinism, a kind of atrophy of the body and also of the

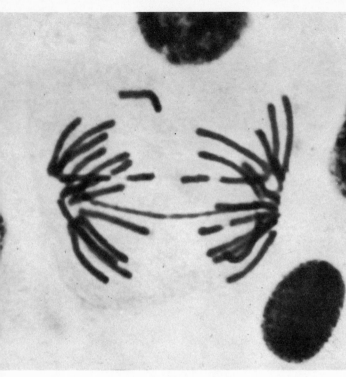

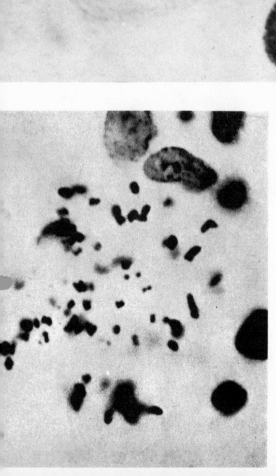

9 The effect of a chemical substance (a nitrogen mustard) on the chromosomes of a tumour cell. (Photograph by Professor P. C. Koller, Chester Beatty Research Institute)

The effect of X-rays on the chromosomes of a broad bean cell. (Photograph by Dr S. H. Revell, Chester Beatty Research Institute.) The photograph shows (a) a chromosome fragment on upper right; (b) a chromosome bridge between the two separating sets of chromosomes

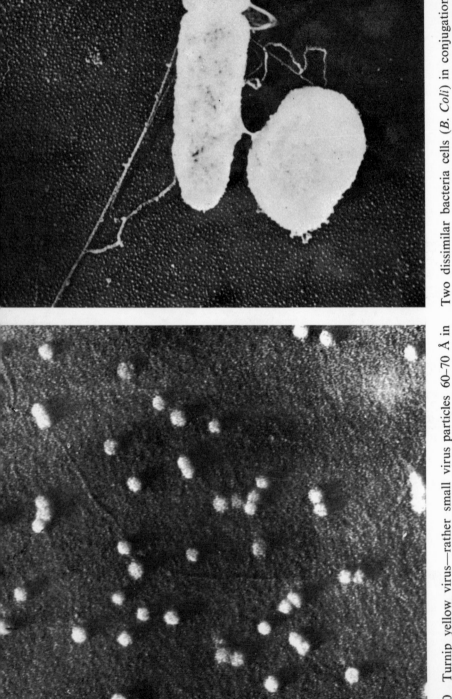

10 Turnip yellow virus—rather small virus particles 60–70 Å in diameter. Photograph by Dr Mercer Chester Beatty Research

Two dissimilar bacteria cells (*B. Coli*) in conjugation. A 'bridge' is formed between them through which they

mental faculties. It was found by Murray in 1891, that this condition could be relieved by feeding sheep's thyroid. The active substance in the thyroid extracts was isolated by E. C. Kendall in 1916, and in the course of time its structure was established, and it was finally synthesized in 1927 by Barger and Harington. It is a comparatively simple substance, a compound of iodine and a common amino-acid, tyrosine. Because of this, the thyroid gland is the reservoir of most of the iodine in the body. If the water supply is deficient in iodine, as happens in some limestone districts, the thyroid is unable to make enough thyroxine and it increases in size in an effort to make up the deficiency. This produces goitre, once a common disease in mountain areas.

Thyroxine is concerned with the oxidation of fats and proteins. When it is absent, the body does not develop properly, giving rise to cretinism. Over-activity of the thyroid causes protuberant eyes and a kind of feverish activity. It is necessary for the metamorphosis of the lower animals. With the thyroid gland removed, tadpoles cannot metamorphose into frogs. On the other hand, when small quantities of thyroxine are added to the water, tadpoles will change prematurely into miniature frogs. It is intimately connected with the secretion of milk. Injection of thyroxine into cows markedly increases both their milk and their fat production—at least temporarily; and it has been found that feeding iodinated proteins, which probably help the cow to make thyroxine, has a similar effect.

The pancreas is another organ which produces substances necessary for health, as well as the digestive enzymes it pours into the intestine. If it is damaged or removed, serious bodily changes occur, especially an inability to oxidize sugar, which then accumulates in the blood. This is what happens in the disease diabetes, which is due to an impaired action of the pancreas. It was found that this condition was relieved by extracts of pancreas from animals, and in 1921 Banting and Best in Toronto isolated from the pancreas a protein called insulin. Actually it is present in separate parts of the pancreas, distinct from the enzyme-producing parts, known as the islets of Langerhans. Only a fraction of a milligram of insulin is required each day by a healthy person, and diabetics can be kept going indefinitely by injections of ox or swine insulin.

One of the first to benefit from insulin was Dr R. D. Lawrence, who has since become one of the foremost authorities on diabetes. In 1922 during an operation, a bone splinter flew into and injured his right eye. The wound turned septic and he became very ill. His illness was eventually diagnosed as diabetes, and he was considered a hopeless case. He went to Florence to spend what time he had left and

F

while there, in the spring of 1923, he heard of the discovery of insulin and at once went to obtain the treatment. He soon recovered and has been able to lead a normal and productive life during the last 26 years.

As we have seen (Fig. 3), insulin is a very complex substance and has not yet been synthesized, and until this has been achieved diabetics will remain dependent on the supplies of insulin which can be obtained from animals.

Above the kidneys are two small glands, known as the suprarenals. Each suprarenal consists of two distinct glands, as their inner parts have quite a different function from the outer layers. It was found in 1895 by Oliver and Schäfer that extracts of the inner part produced very marked physiological actions, and some years afterwards an active substance called adrenaline was isolated from them. In due course the structure of adrenaline was found; it has been synthesized, and the synthetic product has exactly the same action as the natural substance. It is also quite a simple substance. Introduced into the blood-stream, it causes an increase in the blood-pressure, a quickening of the heart-beat, and an increase of blood sugar. It tones up the body and makes it ready to meet unusual stresses. The gland is stimulated by the sympathetic nervous system. Strong mental stresses such as fear, anger, and strong emotion, all cause it to secrete adrenaline into the bloodstream. The result is to stimulate the heart and prepare the body to meet unusual demands upon it. The gland thus acts as a kind of relay station—an intermediary between the brain and the chemical regulating mechanisms. The tiny nervous impulses from the brain enter the gland and cause it to release the hormone, which is carried by the blood to all parts of the body. This is naturally a relatively slow process, and when adrenaline has been released its effects only wear off slowly, so that when you have had a fright your heart continues to palpitate for some time after the cause has disappeared.

The outer layers of this gland produces quite different substances. It was not until 1931 that Swingle and Pfiffner succeeded in preparing stable extracts of the cortical hormones which would maintain life in an animal deprived of the gland. Soon after that, crystalline substances were obtained in several laboratories and their chemical nature was worked out. They belong to a group of substances called steroids which have the same rather unusual hydrocarbon nucleus, which is the central structural feature of a number of apparently unrelated compounds (see Appendix, Fig. 7, III). It turns up in the bile-acids, in vitamin D, and in the sex hormones which are mentioned below.

At least six of these compounds have been isolated from the suprarenal cortex. Some of them seem to be concerned with the breakdown of carbohydrates and proteins. When given in excess they have an anti-insulin effect and cause a rise of blood sugar which amounts to temporary diabetes. Others are concerned in maintaining the balance of inorganic salts in the body—the preponderance of sodium and chloride in the fluids of the body and of potassium and phosphate in the cells.

It was found by Dr Philip S. Hench, of the Mayo Clinic, that one of the first group of substances, namely, cortisone or compound E originally isolated by E. S. Kendall, has a palliative effect on some types of rheumatoid arthritis. Unfortunately the supply of cortisone from suprarenal glands is very small and the expense of treating only a few patients with gland extracts was enormous. The substance can be obtained synthetically from a bile-acid but the development of a method of manufacture has been shortened by the discovery that many plants contain steroids which can be converted into cortisone in fewer steps.

One important function of cortisone and other steroids made by the adrenal cortex is to protect the tissues against the effects of stress. The mechanism of this is unknown, but the increased cellular action required after shock and injuries depends upon the presence of these substances.

We come now to the hormones secreted by the male and female sexual organs. They govern the sexual cycles and all the processes of reproduction. They also determine the secondary sexual characters. A hundred years ago Berthoud showed that the sex glands of a cock transplanted into a hen caused her to develop a cock's comb. The capon develops only a rudimentary comb, but the male sex hormone from any species, even in minute amounts, causes its full development. Males have been known to turn into females, and *vice versa*, when their sex glands are atrophied and injured. Maleness and femaleness is the result of a hormonal balance which is easily disturbed.

Similarly extracts from the ovaries have a powerful effect in causing females to 'come on heat'. A number of substances (oestrogens) have been isolated which produce this effect to a greater or lesser degree. The sex hormones are, in general, very similar to each other—in fact the differences between the characteristic male and female hormones are minor ones.

Finding out how these compounds are related to each other is like solving a complicated jig-saw puzzle in which many of the pieces are missing. Quite a number of synthetic compounds which are not present in the living organism also act as oestrogens. Some are surprisingly simple—for example, the compound stilboestrol, which was discovered by Lawson and Dodds to be more active than the natural hormone. What common characteristics these molecules have has not been discovered.

The last source of hormones I shall mention is the pituitary gland—a complex gland situated in a bony hollow at the base of the skull. The posterior portion of the gland controls the amount of water retained by the body by regulating its flow through the kidneys. The effects of the anterior portion are so extensive that it has been called by Sir Walter Langdon Brown 'the conductor of the whole endocrine orchestra'. It stimulates, and indeed is necessary for, the action of most of the other glands, since it is found that if the anterior part of the gland is removed, the thyroid, the suprarenal cortex, the islets of Langerhans, and the ovaries or testes all atrophy. It controls growth, in that an excess of pituitary action causes gigantism, while a deficiency is dwarfing. A number of distinct hormones have been isolated having distinct actions in stimulating the various hormone-producing glands.

There is a hormone which stimulates the sex glands; others which stimulate milk production, and still others which control various phases of the sexual cycle and control growth. One of them (adreno cortico tropin—ACTH) stimulates the adrenal cortex to liberate the hormones which protect the body from the effects of stress, and relieve the symptoms of rheumatism. This pituitary substance is much too rare and costly for general use in relieving rheumatism—400,000 pigs being required to yield one pound of the hormone! Unlike most of the others, the pituitary hormones are proteins, but Dr C. H. Li has found that in some of them the protein molecule is made up of smaller parts which possess the activity.

The chemical control of the body thus presents a very complicated picture and much remains to be learnt about it. The ductless glands produce a wide variety of substances and their actions are far from simple. A single hormone may be concerned in a great variety of different processes, and the glands also interact with each other. The pituitary, as we have seen, acts as a stimulator of the others; the proper working of the body always depends on a delicate balance of the working of the various glands.

Since they are often quite simple compounds, and are also, generally speaking, indifferent to species, the hormones seem to be relics of a primitive system of control. The thyroxin of the frog is the same as that of cows and human beings. The sex hormones of the fowl are much the same as those of the horse. Very little is known about how they work and what constituents of the body they act on. The only clue in this direction so far is the observations by Prof and Mrs Cori in St Louis, that insulin and the secretion of the pituitary gland both affect the action of an enzyme, hexokinase, which is concerned with oxidizing sugar. They act on it in opposite directions, so that the functioning of hexokinase depends on a correct balance between the two. This is one of the first glimpses we have of a complex interplay of enzymes and hormones through which the bodily functions are regulated and controlled.

XI

Antibodies and Immunity

꙰

Without special means of protection large organisms could not live very long in a world full of parasitic bacteria and viruses. It is difficult to think of a more perfect breeding ground for them than animal tissues and fluids. One method of protection developed by bacteria themselves and by fungi is the use of antibiotics—substances which prevent the growth of foreign bacteria and so secure for their possessor a certain amount of living space. It is possible that animals and plants have on their outer surfaces antibiotic substances which inhibit fungal growths—but such have not been clearly demonstrated.

The skin or outer layer of cells is hard and impervious which helps to keep parasitic particles out of the organism, but it is not sufficient to prevent the accidental entry of micro-organisms through scratches and cuts and through the softer tissues of the alimentary canal. For this reason, it has been necessary for animals to develop other means of protection against the invasion of the body by foreign organisms.

The facts which imply the existence of internal protective agents have been known from early times. It is common knowledge that when an individual has recovered from an infectious disease like measles or mumps, he is immune from a second attack even if he receives another infection. It was also found that with certain diseases which occur in two forms, one mild and the other virulent, infection with the mild form often confers immunity against the virulent form. This was the case with cowpox and smallpox and in some countries it has long been a practice to seek to be infected with cowpox for the sake of immunity against the more serious disease. In England vaccination with cowpox to confer immunity against smallpox was introduced successfully by Edward Jenner. The same line of thought led to the attempt to produce mild strains of a disease for the specific purpose of conferring immunity.

Experiments with laboratory animals showed that the injection of killed or damaged bacteria or viruses (vaccines) sometimes conferred immunity against infection by living bacteria. In making preparations of this kind it is necessary to be sure that all the bacteria are destroyed, to the extent that they are incapable of multiplication; but at the same time their ability to cause immunity must be retained. This is obviously a rather tricky business and instead of killing the bacteria by heating, treatment with chemicals such as formalin is used in the preparation of vaccines. For example a successful vaccine against poliomyelitis has been produced by treatment of the virus with formalin.

From innumerable experiments of this kind it was concluded that the body responds to the introduction of foreign organisms by producing substances called antibodies, which are able in some way to neutralize or destroy the foreign bodies. The course of a typical infectious disease is (1) infection, (2) multiplication of the infective agent, (3) antibody formation which, if it is extensive enough, may lead to the neutralization and destruction of the agent.

In some cases once formed, the antibodies or the ability to make them may remain in the body of the recovered person for considerable periods and even for all the rest of his life and, in that case, he will probably be immune from the disease if he receives another infection. However, in other diseases, such as influenza, immunity is only conferred for a limited period, i.e. the antibodies formed are lost or become ineffective.

It is obvious that in this reaction animals have developed a very effective means of destroying invading micro-organisms. A great deal of research has been done to discover its mechanism and although much still remains to be learnt about it, the main features are now known.

Antibodies are formed in the animal organism when a foreign protein (i.e. a protein from another species) or certain other substances are injected into an animal. These have the power of combining with the foreign substance and in many cases of causing it to be precipitated. Substances which are capable of invoking the production of antibodies are called *antigens*. They include not only proteins (and some proteins are better antigens than others) but also complex carbohydrates. The reaction between an antigen and its antibody is highly specific and also quantitative, i.e. a quantity of antibody will combine with a definite quantity of its own antigen, but not with others.

Bacteria, of course, contain many substances which could act as antigens, but the most effective ones are probably the substances of the cell walls. When antibodies to these are formed they combine with the cell surface and render the bacterium open to attack by scavenger cells in the blood called phagocytes.

Bacteria also produce harmful proteins called toxins, which are often responsible for some of the effects of the disease. These toxins also elicit the formation of antibodies—called antitoxins. Antitoxins can be prepared by inoculating a suitable animal such as the horse with the toxin and they can be used to help a patient—especially in the period before his own antibodies have come into action.

Antibodies are proteins and it has been found that they are present among the blood serum proteins in the fraction which is distinguished as γ-globulin. It is possible that this globulin is made up entirely of the different antibodies which the body possesses. If a person has had measles, his γ-globulin contains the measles antibody and in fact this antibody can be concentrated from the γ-globulin of the blood. This γ-globulin has been prepared for human use from the stocks of blood plasma which are kept for emergency uses and confers immunity against measles. However, it is not possible to separate the measles antibody from others present, and it may be that there are less desirable substances with it so it is not used too freely.

Much research has been carried out in efforts to discover the mechanism of antibody formation. As the antibody is a protein and is produced as a response to the presence in the blood of foreign antigens, it is reasonable to suppose that the antigen is present when its antibody is made. The site of the synthesis of antibody is known to be certain cells of the lymphatic system which are present in various parts of the body. The antibodies pass into the blood through the lymphatic vessels.

As I mentioned above, the relation between an antibody and its antigen is highly specific. Much work has been done to discover the limits of the specificity of the antigen-antibody reaction. An antigen can be modified slightly by having small chemical groups added to it. When antibodies were mixed with slightly changed antigens it was found by Landsteiner that they were capable of detecting very small modifications of the antigen, such as the addition of a small chemical group.

However, the exact way in which the antigen influences the synthesis of the antibody protein is not known. It has been suggested that as the antibodies are all proteins of a similar nature, they are kept, as it were, in a semi-fabricated state, like suits of clothes in certain 'ready-to-wear' tailoring shops, waiting for the final touches which will ensure an exact fit, to be put on in the presence of the antigen. It has also been thought that this modification of the antibodies to suit particular antigens consists only in local modifications of the folding of the protein chains. Attempts have been made by Pauling and Campbell to produce artificial antibodies by incubating 'denatured' ox globulin with an antigen. A material was obtained which was capable of precipitating the antigenic substance, but it is not certain that this was a real antibody similar to those produced in life.

If the antigen has to be present when the antibody is formed, we have to suppose that in those cases in which immunity lasts for life, the antigen also remains in the tissues as a 'pattern' all this time— not withstanding the fact that we know that the lymph cells in which the antibodies are formed are changed many times.

DISORDERS ARISING FROM THE IMMUNITY MECHANISM

The immunity mechanism is in some ways too efficient, because in some rather special cases it leads to undesired reactions. For example, there is the phenomenon known as 'allergy'. An individual may become sensitive to a foreign protein, which may be quite common in his surroundings. His blood will contain antibodies to this substance and, as a result, the immunity reaction occurs whenever he is exposed to it. This leads to various uncomfortable and sometimes very troublesome effects, which are similar to those which occur with infection. The temperature may rise (fever) and *histamine* is liberated in the tissues. It is this which causes 'hay fever' and the characteristic skin weals of some allergic reactions.

It also became known, when attempts were made to perform blood transfusion, that the blood of two individuals of the same species frequently cannot be mixed, because agglutination occurs. This led to a number of blood groups being distinguished and the recognition that the blood of a donor should be of the same group as that of the receiver.

The agglutination is caused by substances analogous to antibodies which are present in the serum. These antibodies, or agglutinins as they are called, are naturally compatible with the corpuscles of their own type of blood, but they cause agglutination with other types, through a reaction which is similar to the antigen-antibody reaction.

Four main groups of blood have been recognized which are labelled as follows:

Corpuscles (antigens)	O	A	B	AB
Plasma antibodies (agglutinins)	$\alpha\beta$	β	α	—

The blood group O contains antibodies to both A and B. For this reason it will agglutinate blood of groups A, B and also AB. On the other hand the serum of A and B is not capable of agglutinating corpuscles of type O, because group O corpuscles are not antigens for the A and B antibodies.

The blood of group AB contains no antibodies, so that an individual with this blood can receive blood from any other group without harmful effects. On the other hand, if it is given to an individual having blood of any other group, it will be agglutinated because all these bloods contain its antibodies.

This is a very complicated situation and we may wonder how it came about. The different blood groups are controlled by genes, so that the blood group of each person is determined by that of his parents in accordance with the Mendelian laws of heredity. It would seem likely that the present blood groups are derived from quite distinct ancestral strains of the human race, but they go back to a stage long before the development of the present races of mankind as the distinction of blood groups is not to any great extent a matter of race.

It would be expected that if an individual inherited from his parents two incompatible components of blood, he would not survive and that, in the course of time, genic incompatibility would be eliminated. However, some other antigenic components of blood have been recognized, which are also inherited by Mendelian rules. One of these is the so-called 'Rhesus factor' which has been found to be present in 83 per cent of the population of England and about 85 per cent of the white population of New York, and may lead to incompatibility between the blood of the unborn child and that of the mother if she does not possess it and her husband does. The human placenta is not a perfect barrier against the passage of antibodies and in some cases antigens from the foetus may pass into the blood stream of the mother and there give rise to the formation of antibodies. If these find their way back into the child, they produce a disastrous reaction (haemolytic disease of the new born).

Another example of the immunity mechanism being too efficient has been found in attempts to graft skin from one person to another. An individual can replace a certain amount of lost skin by growth from the edges of the wound inwards. If the area of skin lost is very great, this process is rarely successfully completed. The task of making so much new skin is too much for the resources of the injured person. It is possible to help the growth of new skin by grafting skin from other uninjured parts of the individual's own body. This can be taken off in thin layers which do not cause a serious injury and they help to cover the wound and act as centres from which new skin cells are formed. It would be a great help if skin taken from other individuals could also be grafted. It would then be possible to keep skin banks for use in accidents. But it has been found, both with human beings and animals, that although such grafts appear to be quite happy for a few days, after this some reaction takes place and the foreign skin is sloughed off. When a graft of a foreign skin is tried a second time the wound rejects it from the start.

This is an immune reaction. The body reacts to the skin of another individual of the same species by producing antibodies (a process which takes a few days) and these react with the grafted skin and cause it to shrivel up. When the antibodies have already been formed in a previous grafting operation this reaction is immediate.

This is an even more highly specific response than the antibody response to foreign proteins which was discussed above, as it distinguishes between the different individual members of one species. Practically the only exception is the case of identical twins, which are able to exchange skin grafts whether they are human beings or cattle. In fact this provides a conclusive test (nearly 100 per cent true) for identical twins.

It is an extremely remarkable phenomenon. Why should the immunity mechanism be capable of distinguishing between distinct (i.e. not identical) individuals? The way in which the individual members of a species differ is in their genetic constitution. As we have seen, the hereditary character of an individual, as derived from the parents, is determined by the genes he inherits. The collection of genes which any individual receives from each parent is determined in the crossing-over process, which, as we have seen, gives him a selection of the genes carried by the parents. It follows that, except for identical twins (which have arisen from one fertilized egg and therefore have the same genetic constitution), the chances are that practically every individual human being will be genetically different from all others. This would not be the case in inbred animal colonies, derived from a single pair, in which after a time the same or a nearly similar genetic constitution may be established, but human communities have not reached this condition.

These facts have been well understood for a long time. The surprising and new finding is that the antibody mechanism can distinguish the differences of genetic constitution of individual members of a species. An antibody reaction occurs whenever a foreign gene is introduced.

Since the antibody-forming mechanism is so sensitive, we should now ask why it does not respond to the individual's own genes or proteins. How does it know that a particular protein is its own; or that a piece of tissue belongs to it and is not 'foreign'? This may arise from the fact that the power of producing an immunological response is one which develops very late in the development of the individual. It was known that embryos do not have the ability to make antibodies. Thus it appeared that all the antigens which are present in the embryo when the immunological apparatus begins to function produce no response and only those antigens which are introduced afterwards can make antibodies. In 1949 F. M. Burnet[1] and F. Fenner followed this idea up with the suggestion that, if foreign substances were introduced into the embryo during the pre-immunological stage, they would also be tolerated, i.e. they would not be treated as 'foreign' antigens when the antibody machinery begins to function.

This has been confirmed in laboratory experiments by Medawar and his associates. They found that if cells from a strain CBA of brown mice are injected into a white of another strain A while the latter are still in embryo, it will, when adult, accept skin grafts of the former. This is a convincing demonstration that the antibody mechanism does not respond to substances which have been present in the embryo state. In fact, it is found that this state of 'tolerance' also persists for a few days after birth. In the case of birds, it can be produced by injecting the foreign material into the egg. Exactly how the antibody-producing cells become unresponsive to the proteins which were present in the embryo is still unknown and must wait for further knowledge of the actual mechanism of production of antibodies.

There is another way—a rather drastic one—in which individuals can be made unresponsive to foreign proteins and grafts of other individuals. If the individual is subjected to a sub-lethal dose of X-rays, the antibody mechanism is disorganized and for a time the injection of foreign proteins will be tolerated, i.e. no antibodies will be formed. This of course has its own dangers, because it leaves the organism defenceless against bacteria, etc, and in fact, after receiving a substantial dose of radiation, many animals die of infection. But it also makes it possible to introduce foreign bodies such as red marrow cells, which, as we have seen, will help to keep the individual going until it has repaired its own machinery for making red blood cells. During the interval at which the animal is being helped by foreign cells, it is what is known as a *chimera*, i.e. a composite of cells of more than one genetic origin.

[1] Now Sir Macfarlane Burnet, OM.

XII

Cancer

꒳

The growth of an animal organism is, as we have seen, very accurately controlled. Every kind of cell keeps in place and in step with the others. We might wonder what would happen if the controlling mechanism, whatever it is, were to break down so that some cells just went on multiplying without stopping. This is precisely what happens with malignant cells, which form cancers. Not only do they escape from the control of the organism, but they often infiltrate through tissues other than the one in which they originated. They may also find their way with the blood stream or the lymph into many other tissues and they finally cause death, either by interfering with the working of the body or by taking all the available nourishment and so starving the rest of the body.

At the present time one person in six in Britain and one in seven in the United States die of cancer. An enormous amount of work has been done to try to discover why cancerous cells escape the normal body controls; and also to find ways of killing them without destroying too many healthy cells at the same time. However, until we know what mechanism controls cell multiplication in a healthy body, it will be difficult and perhaps impossible to specify what has gone wrong in a cancerous growth.

Nevertheless, a great deal of information about the origin of cancer (carcinogenesis) has been found, and it is probable that many of the relevant facts are known, although it is not yet possible to fit them all into a coherent pattern.

Numerous theories of the origin of cancer have been put forward, all of which can produce some facts and observations which they are able to explain. These theories fall into three types:

(1) *The Mutation Theory:* According to this, a cell in the body undergoes a mutation as a result of which it becomes essentially a different kind of cell. Of course many changes of this type will produce cells which cannot live or at least are unable to multiply. But

according to the theory, occasionally a new type of cell is formed which can escape from the normal body controls, and thus will be able to invade and replace other tissues of the body.

The most cogent fact in favour of this theory is the discovery that a number of chemical substances cause cancer and these substances have usually also been found to be mutagens, they are capable of producing definite mutations when applied, for example, to the sperm of flies or to fungi.

This discovery is undoubtedly one of the great milestones in cancer research. It was known in the nineteenth century that cancer was common among certain types of workers, such as chimney sweeps and cotton spinners, who used a particular kind of oil for lubricating the spindles, and workers in the shale oil fields. However, it was not till after 1920 that attempts were made to find the chemical substances responsible. In 1921, Block and Dreifuss of Zurich showed that the active substance in coal tar was concentrated in the higher boiling fractions. The first identification of active compounds was achieved in 1932 by Kennaway, Hieger and Mayneord. It had been found in the study of tars that the activity seemed to be associated with a particular kind of fluorescence spectrum. This was followed up and eventually it was discovered by Hieger that the pure hydrocarbon substance, 1-2 benzathracene, possessed this kind of spectrum. This led to the synthesis of a large number of similar hydrocarbons by Cook and eventually pure hydrocarbons, which produce skin cancers in mice and rats, were isolated from tar and also made synthetically. A fair number of such hydrocarbons have since been identified.

More recently, it has been found that many other types of chemical compounds are capable of causing cancer—sometimes in one organ, sometimes in another. The list of known carcinogens has become quite extensive (see Appendix, Fig. 8). It includes certain dye stuffs (e.g. butter yellow) and also intermediates used in the dye industry, like naphthylamine, which were found to be responsible for bladder cancer which has been common among workers in the dye industry.

Most of these substances have also been found to be mutagens. This is the case with compounds of the 'mustard' series, which have already been mentioned as the first chemicals to be shown to have the ability to produce mutations (see p. 63). But numerous other types of carcinogens have since been shown to be mutagens, so that there is at least a close connection between carcinogenicity and the ability to cause mutations. One characteristic of mutagens is that they are capable of reaching the genetic material in the nucleus of the cell and of reacting with it. Some of these substances react very readily with the nucleic acid (DNA) of the chromosomes; and when such reactions occur, the normal mechanism of cell division may be upset, and also the message carried by the genic code may also be interfered with.

Because such reactions occur, some carcinogenic chemicals are used extensively as *anticancer* agents. They interfere with cell division and may diminish the rate of growth altogether. The destruction of cancer cells by drugs is, however, a very difficult problem. A successful anticancer agent is one which attacks cancer cells, while leaving normal cells relatively unharmed. One of the few distinctive characteristics of cancer cells is that they are multiplying rapidly, so that it would appear that the most likely approach would be to destroy cells while they are in the process of cell division. The most likely anticancer agents are those which interfere with cell division and these are also usually mutagens.

It was pointed out by Haddow that most carcinogens are also anticancer agents. This might seem to be a paradox, but it must be remembered that the initiation of a cancerous growth is a very rare event. These substances more frequently cause other kinds of damage to the living cells, so that their use as anticancer agents is quite feasible.

Ionising radiations such as X-rays and radiations from radioactive substances also conform with this rule. It was in fact discovered very soon after Roentgen's discovery of X-rays that they not only cause serious 'burns', which frequently become malignant; but they can also, when carefully employed, be used to destroy malignant growths. In many ways these radiations are an ideal method of dealing with malignant growths near the surface of the body. The cancer cells are more sensitive to the radiations than normal healthy cells usually are, so that it is possible to destroy them without injuring healthy tissue too much; and it is possible to localize the exposure to a considerable extent. However, X-rays are not invariably successful as a small proportion of the cancer cells may escape, especially when secondary growths have started, and these may be a centre for new malignant growths. For this reason, if it could be achieved, treatment by drugs which would specifically destroy malignant cells is much to be desired, but only limited successes have been achieved so far. The most successful agents used so far, apart from radiations, are:

(i) *compounds of the 'mustard' series,* which, as already mentioned, are mutagens and are capable of reacting with the chromosomes.

(ii) *antipurines*; these are substances which are very similar to the normal components of DNA. They become incorporated in DNA, but when this has occurred, they do not function properly so that cell division is inhibited.

The cancer cell may be vulnerable while in the act of cell division, but once formed, it is rather tough. It is less differentiated than the ordinary cells and lacks their special abilities. It seems that many of the special abilities of the cells from which the cancer originated are lost, and all that is left is a high ability to grow and multiply. The cancer cell is in fact usually an aggressive cell which is able to push its way into other tissues. The cancer cell is often less responsive to the immunity mechanism than normal cells—it is often possible to graft a cancerous growth from one animal to another of the same species. This has enormously assisted cancer research because tumours of a standard kind can be multiplied at will by grafting small pieces into healthy animals.

(2) *Virus Theory of Cancer.* Many attempts have been made to extract a non-living agent from tumours which is capable to giving rise to tumours when injected into animals. In most cases, if the extracts are free from living cells, no successful transmission of the tumour has been achieved. However, Murphy and Peyton Rous in 1910 found that it was possible to transmit certain *avian* tumours, by injecting cell-free extracts of the tumour cells into healthy birds. These extracts contained the submicroscopic particles of the cytoplasm but they certainly did not contain living cells. It was concluded that these extracts contain an agent or virus which causes the disease.

Another example was the Shope papilloma virus of rabbits. These are non-malignant growths, which occasionally become malignant, found in the rabbits of New Jersey and from them Shope succeeded in extracting a virus, which was capable of producing growths in healthy rabbits.

However, although many attempts have been made to do so, it has not been possible to produce cell-free agents, which will cause the disease, in more than a few types of cancer.

Nevertheless, some workers adhere to the theory that cancer is essentially a virus disease. It is suggested, for example, that apparently healthy cells harbour the virus but it is only when the cell becomes weakened or diseased that the virus can act effectively. Or it is suggested that the carcinogenic chemicals act by reducing the resistance of the cell, so that the virus already present becomes effective. Another version of the same theory is that the change from a normal to a cancer cell is due to the modification of some of the cytoplasmic particles which are normally present. It might be that the carcinogenic substances give rise to a change in the nature of some of these par-

11 Bacteriophage attacking a bacterium (*B. Coli*). Photograph by
Dr R. W. G. Wyckoff. The picture shows two cells. The cell above
has only just begun to be attacked, while that below appears to be
disrupted

12 A later stage of the attack of Bacteriophage on *B. Coli*. The picture shows a cell full of newly formed bacteriophage particles

ticles, which is inherited from one particle to another.

On the whole, however, it can be said that the virus theory of cancer meets with great difficulties, except in those cases where a virus agent can be demonstrated. In other cases it is implied either that a dormant virus is normally present, which only becomes active when stimulated in some way, or that one of the normal cell particles becomes a virus when it is acted on by a carcinogenic substance. There is no doubt that the carcinogenic substance can act on the cell particles present in the cytoplasm, but very little is known at present about how their behaviour is changed and whether such changes could be transmitted from one cell to its descendants.

(3) *Metabolic Theories of Cancer.* It is an undoubted fact that cancer cells behave differently from the normal cells in which they originate. Much work has been done on these differences, but few really characteristic effects have been found. It is found, however, that the activity of some enzyme systems is increased and that of others is diminished. These differences are often so great that the cancer cell lives in an essentially different way to the normal cells. Warburg and others have shown, for example, that the cancer cell obtains its energy, not like most normal tissues from the oxidation of sugars, but by a less profound type of splitting of the sugar molecules, known as glycolysis[1]. Warburg has therefore proposed that the carcinogenic agents are in fact cell poisons which interfere with the normal mode of life of the cell and compel it to adopt a new mode in order to live. The change from the normal to the cancer type on this theory is the cell's effort to continue to live when its normal mode of life is interfered with. One result of this effort is that it is stimulated to an abnormal rate of cell division.

There is no doubt that many cells are adaptable to changes in their environment. It was shown by Hinshelwood that bacteria in particular are very good at adapting themselves to a new way of life. They can grow in the presence of dyes which interfere with their ordinary mode of living. There is usually a 'lag' period in which the cells are adapting themselves to the new conditions. During this, new systems of enzymes are formed and new methods of synthesis are found to replace those which have been blocked by the dye. According to the metabolic theory, the cancer cell is an adaptation to new conditions—a response to the loss of normal functioning. According to this view, carcinogenic substances act by interfering with enzyme systems which the cell normally uses. They act indeed as selective poisons and they compel the cell, in order to continue to exist, to find an alternative way of living.

[1] See p. 47.

However, chemical poisons are not the only agents which cause cancers. It was found by Dr Oppenheimer that if plastic substances are embedded in the skin of an animal, a cancerous growth may be formed. The nature of the plastic seems to be quite unimportant, but if the plastic film is pierced with holes, no cancer may occur. It seems, therefore, that the cancerous growth is due to interference with the flow of oxygen and food materials and to the effort of the cells to improvise an alternative way of living.

Cancers may also be formed by continual irritation of a tissue or if a wound is prevented from healing. It is possible that lip cancers caused by contact with pipe stems are due to this, but chemical action by tobacco tar is also a possibility.

(4) *Cancer due to Hormonal Disturbances.* Somewhat similar in origin are cancers due to hormonal disturbances, which are common in older men and women. Many bodily processes, as we have seen, are controlled by hormones and require an accurate balance of hormonal actions, if they are to function properly. We have also seen that the glands which produce hormones are themselves controlled by other glands, such as the pituitary. In ageing individuals, the proper balance of hormones may be upset and an abnormal growth of glands may occur, either by overstimulation or because the gland is making an effort to produce sufficient quantities of a hormone which are required.

Mammary cancers are very common in certain strains of female mice, but removal of the ovaries reduces the incidence of the mammary tumours. It follows that some substance produced in the ovaries stimulates the occurrence of mammary tumours. In the same way, breast cancer of women is sometimes successfully treated by removal of the ovaries; similarly tumours of the prostate gland of males is sometimes treated by castration. It is found that much can be done in cases in which tumours are the result of the hormonal (or endocrine) system being out of balance by restoring the balance by suitable hormone therapy.

It has also been possible to replace hormones by the synthetic equivalent. In fact, one of the most successful chemical treatments of cancer is by the synthetic oestrogens (see p. 166) used for cancers of the breast and the prostate.

CONCLUSIONS

It will be obvious that the subject of cancer is a large and very complex one and there are many different facets to the whole problem. It is quite possible that cancer is not one phenomenon but many, that different types of cancer have distinct origins which do not have a great deal in common. On the other hand, it may be that there is a single pattern, the nature of which is still unknown, which underlies the different manifestations; and that the different theories outlined above, which emphasize one or other of the different features, all express a certain aspect of whole truth.

Cancer is not like an infectious disease in which, once the agent has been identified, measures of control or cure can often be devised, and the natural defence mechanisms of the body can also be stimulated. It is essentially a disease of organization and as such it is probably peculiar to the higher forms of life. To understand it we obviously need to know much more about the way in which the normal healthy organism works. We have seen that cancers can be produced by extraneous agents acting on the body cells. The fact that the incidence of different types of cancer varies very considerably from one country to another shows that it is to a considerable extent a disease produced by environmental conditions, and as such it ought to be possible to reduce the incidence very considerably when the causative agents have been recognized. It is well known that human beings are subjected to ionizing radiation from cosmic rays, which may be expected to produce a certain incidence of cancer. In thirty years, at sea level, the dose from this source is about one roentgen. In some localities there is also a quite appreciable amount of radioactivity in the ground and in drinking water, which would have to be taken into account. As we have seen radioactive substances like radium and radiothorium (and also strontium from atomic bombs) are concentrated in the bone, where they may remain for long periods and eventually cause bone cancers.

We might ask whether cancer would occur if these environmental influences were eliminated. Do cancers arise spontaneously in an apparently healthy organism? Since a fair number of chemical substances have been found to be carcinogenic, it may be that the organism itself may produce carcinogenic substances, either in its normal operations or through some errors of metabolism. The weak carcinogenicity of one normal constituent of the body, *cholesterol*, which is present in fats, has been demonstrated by Hieger. While the function of this substance is unknown, it is rather curious that it is related chemically to the steroid sex hormones and it might be that it is a by-product of the formation of these substances.

It can hardly be asserted that the body has developed any natural defence mechanisms against cancer, but the fact that the incidence of cancer increases rapidly with age, suggests either that as the body ages, the controlling mechanisms become weaker, so that it is easier for cancer cells to originate or that, in young vigorous organisms the cancer cell is unable to establish itself, i.e. the controlling mechanism is strong enough to control it. It is a curious fact that, in some instances, cancers cannot be recognized for a long time after the carcinogenic agent has been introduced. There is a long 'lag' period during which the carcinogenic agent is present, but apparently has no effect.

XIII

The Origin of Life and Photosynthesis

The smallest body which possesses all the characteristics of life, the cell, is quite obviously an extremely complicated structure. At its simplest it contains at least two or three complex and interlocking cycles of activity, which are concerned with the breakdown of food materials and with the formation of high-energy and other intermediates which are used for the synthesis of the characteristic compounds. The agents which bring about these changes are themselves formed from the products. Apart from all this basic chemical activity, there are also the special arrangements by which cell division occurs.

In trying to discover how systems of such complication came into existence in the first place, it is probably hopeless to look at cells as they exist now, because they have an enormously lengthy history behind them. Unfortunately, in our present day world, we do not find any intermediate steps, except perhaps viruses (which are a special case and a product of cells) which would help to bridge the gap between the living and the non-living.

Yet all life must have originated and been elaborated on the earth. There must have been a time when the earth was too hot for any living things as we know them. The igneous rocks underlying the present superficial strata bear evidence of having crystallized out from a molten magma. The stratified rocks which overlie them bear witness in their fossil relics to the long history of life on the earth and many of them—the chalks, corals and limestones are actual residues of former life on the planet. But the earliest stages are missing from the fossil record, and it is probable that something approaching life as we know it at present had already been evolved before any enduring traces were left.

It might have been expected that if the original processes which led to living structures were completely natural, they would still be taking place and that we should find, somewhere in the world, processes which might be thought to represent at least a step or two in the elaboration of living forms.

It is a very curious thing that, with one or two exceptions, practically no intermediate stages between simple inorganic substances and living things or their products are known to exist. Practically all the organic substances on the earth are products of life. It is possible that the hydrocarbon oils which exist very plentifully in some strata are an exception, but this is uncertain and it is quite likely that they are to a considerable extent themselves the products of highly developed life, like the coal deposits. This is demonstrated by the fact that, in some cases, they contain 'optically active' compounds, i.e. when two possible forms of a compound exist, which are mirror images of each other, only one occurs. This is an indication of living origin, because natural processes (except crystallization) do not usually distinguish between the two optically active forms of one molecule.

We do not find organic compounds being elaborated by any process which does not involve life anywhere in the world.

We are forced to adopt one of three alternatives:

(1) *Life did not originate in this world.* As Arrhenius suggested, when he was confronted with the difficulty of finding sufficient time for the evolution of life, it might have arrived from other worlds in the form of spores. However, this only shifts the difficulty of accounting for the origin of life to other places, and in any case the evidence of cosmology suggests that the earth has existed for an appreciable fraction of the period of existence of the whole universe.

(2) *Life did originate on this world,* but the conditions at the surface of the earth have altered so greatly, that reactions leading to life no longer occur. This view has been put forward and supported by the Russian scientist, A. I. Oparin, in a book on *The Origin of Life,* which was first published in an English translation in 1938. Oparin argues that in the early stages of the earth's history, the surface rocks contained considerable quantities of metallic carbides, which, by reacting with water, would form first methane or acetylene and later more complex hydrocarbon compounds. This would provide an 'organic' environment, which would be much more favourable to the formation of complex organic compounds than that which exists now. There is evidence for hydrocarbons like methane in the atmospheres of other planets. Methane, as well as ammonia, have been detected in the atmosphere of Jupiter and methane alone in Uranus and Neptune.

Consider what would happen if such an atmosphere were exposed to intense solar radiation. The sun produces not only visible light, but ultra-violet rays, as well as high speed particles (ionizing radiations), which may well have been much more intense in the past than now. These radiations are capable of breaking hydrocarbon molecules into fragments called radicals, which can react with each other and build up into long chain compounds. In the presence of ammonia a great variety of nitrogenous compounds could also be formed in this way. Experiments have been made by Miller in an attempt to reproduce these circumstances. A mixture of water vapour, carbon dioxide and ammonia was exposed to electric discharges and it was found that a variety of compounds including amino acids was formed. If amino acids are formed in a concentrated condition, the effect of further irradiation may well be to cause them to combine into long peptide chains such as occur in proteins. This type of condensation can be effected artificially. It involves (see p. 17) the elimination of water molecules. The water can easily be removed from amino acids, yielding compounds called amino acid anhydrides. Woodward and Schramm have shown that these anhydrides link up spontaneously into peptide chains.

It is of course a long way from this to the exactly organized structures of the natural proteins and we do now know how this gap could be bridged. But it no doubt would help a great deal if we could suppose that at an early stage in the earth's history a surface layer rich in carbon compounds were present. Certainly under such conditions very complex compounds could be formed by the action of solar radiation. Not only could we expect complicated hydrocarbons and organic nitrogen compounds to be formed, but phosphorus too could become activated and attached to organic residues and it might well be that, out of the myriad possible combinations, eventually a simple self-reproducing system would be formed, which would increase its amount by making use of the organic material around it and would thus impose its own pattern on the organic environment.

We have no idea what this primitive self-reproducing system was like or of its transformation towards living structures as we know them. The living cell as we know it is the end of an enormous series of developments, not the beginning. Life itself has entirely destroyed the primitive environment from which it arose and all the intermediate steps. The only possible and likely relic from this stage of the evolution of life might be some of the petroleum deposits—but these again are in sedimentary rocks and may have been formed by living things at a much later date.

(3) *Steps leading to the creation of life from inorganic materials are still going on in the present world,* either in some unsuspected place or on such a small scale that they have not been recognized. We can

only say that if such circumstances exist they remain to be discovered.

We can obtain some clues about the circumstances under which living things originated from our knowledge of their chemical composition.

As I mentioned above, all living things are optically active, i.e. when two forms of a compound are possible only one is present. Thus all the amino-acids present in proteins are of the *l*-configuration. It follows that at some stage or other something must have happened to decide that living things should use compounds with the *l* (left-handed) rather than the reverse *d* (right-handed) configuration.

There are few natural ways which discriminate between these two forms of a compound. As I mentioned above, one of these is crystallization. Some minerals crystallize quite naturally into optically active forms, e.g. quartz crystals are found in either one or the other form and this is also true of other minerals. It is thus possible that life acquired its preference for one configuration (in the case of proteins, the *l*-form) by being associated with a particular kind of crystal. Thus if the original germ of life started in contact with a crystal of quartz (or clay minerals) which had optical activities, it may well be that one of the possible forms of amino acid was made use of and, having been established, the pattern involving this type was continued to the present day. Another way in which this could come about has been suggested by Dr J. H. Northrop, who pointed out that, when organic substances crystallize, they may give optically active crystals (in equal quantities). But when pairs of crystals of opposite sign are formed, they may easily be separated from each other by perfectly natural agencies like the wind, so that localities may occur where an excess exists of organic material of one configuration. It must have been some such accident as this which imprinted on living things their preference for *l*-amino acids. The naturally occurring sugars also are found with particular configurations.

It is probable that there could be a similar family of living things making use of the *d*-compounds—in which all the important compounds were of the opposite configuration. There is no sign of this family on this world, but it might exist on another planet.

It is, however, difficult to reconcile the idea of a primitive organic environment with the amount of oxygen now in the earth's atmosphere. There is in fact plenty of oxygen to burn all the carbon compounds completely to carbon dioxide and water. Under the conditions suggested for the elaboration of complex compounds, oxidation would certainly occur. Even in the present world, few organic substances can remain exposed to the atmosphere and sunshine and water for any length of time without becoming oxidized. We could only get over this difficulty if we suppose that the composition of the atmosphere has also changed with time and that there is much more oxygen now than in previous epochs. Where could oxygen have come from? There is much oxygen and nitrogen in the sun and it is not impossible that atomic particles of these substances which are shot out from the sun are captured by the earth in sufficient quantities to change the atmosphere over long periods of time. Hydrogen is too light to be permanently held in the earth's atmosphere.

LIFE AND ENTROPY

There is no doubt that under the influence of life there has been a great elaboration of complex materials on the earth. Can this be explained as a purely natural process, operating under the known laws of physics? At first sight it seems to be contrary to the tendencies which we observe in the non-living universe. Here the direction in in which spontaneous processes occur is always down-hill; energy always becomes more dissipated; materials always pass from more organized states to more mixed-up states.

This tendency was recognized by Lord Kelvin and formulated as the law of dissipation of energy. Now better known as the second law of thermodynamics, it can be expressed in a number of different ways. One of them, as formulated by Willard Gibbs, makes use of the concept of entropy. Entropy is a measure of mixed-up-ness or disorder, or of the degree of dissipation of energy, and the mathematicians' statement of this law is that entropy is always increased in natural processes which occur of their own accord.

The growth and elaboration of organisms seem at first to be a direct contradiction of this law. We see in living processes an increase in elaboration and order. It is only when the organism dies that disintegration occurse and disorder increases. It would thus seem that the whole progress of life on this planet, which has led to the evolution of more and more complex structures, is contrary to the laws of the inanimate world.

It therefore seems that life has found a way of evading the otherwise universal tendency to dissipation and decay. Kelvin, when he formulated the law of dissipation of energy, made a possible exception in favour of the operations of life. J. N. Lewis thought that living things are 'cheats in the game of entropy'. However, scientific opinion at the present day takes the view that such an exception is unnecessary. The entropy law only requires that *on the whole* energy is dissipated and entropy is increased. There can be a local decrease of entropy and increase in organization if it is compensated by a greater increase of entropy elsewhere.

If we examine the matter more carefully, we find that life is not independent of the great processes of the natural world. All life depends directly on the great outflowing of energy from the sun, which is a dissipative process, by which entropy is increased. Animal life is entirely dependent on plants for food; and plants make direct use of the energy of the sun's radiation. If the sun's rays were cut off, life could not maintain itself for more than a very short time on this planet.

Thus we reach the conclusion that the elaboration of complex living structures is directly dependent on the dissipation of solar energy. There is a local decrease of entropy in the living organism, but it is compensated by a great increase of entropy in the dissipation of radiation from the sun.

PHOTOSYNTHESIS

The basic process on which all life depends is thus the utilization of solar energy for the elaboration of complex compounds. However this originally occurred, it now takes place almost entirely in the photosynthetic apparatus of plants and algae, which have evolved a highly efficient apparatus for making use of the visible radiations arriving from the sun.

The photosynthetic apparatus of green plants makes use of a green pigment called chlorophyll, which is present in small granules called chloroplasts, which exist in the green cells. Chlorophyll is a not remarkably complex molecule, and its structure is largely known. Its most distinctive feature is the presence of a magnesium atom surrounded by four indole groups, making a kind of flat plate.[2] However, chlorophyll is only capable of bringing about photosynthesis when it is in the chloroplast. In recent years much has been learnt about the structure of these bodies from electron microscope photographs of thin sections of them. All the chloroplasts which have been examined show a laminated structure (see Pl. 13), i.e. a system like the sheets of a book packed parallel with each other. Sometimes the sheets or lamellae run through the whole chloroplast but in other cases there are a number of more or less separate piles of sheets. Each lamella is found to consist of two membranes joined at the ends and each membrane is 65 Å thick[1] and the space between them is about the same thickness. This is about the thickness of a small pro-

[1] $1 \text{ Å} = 10^{-8}$ cm.
[2] Similar to haemoglobin (p. 164) with Mg in place of Fe.

tein molecule (see Fig. 17). It is likely that the membranes consist of films of protein with a fatty layer between and it has been suggested that the chlorophyll molecules form a film between the protein and the fatty substance.

It was shown by Hill in 1939 that the primary action which chloroplasts bring about in light is to split water into the two fragments or radicals, H and OH, thus:

$$H_2O \rightarrow H + OH$$

Oxygen is eventually liberated from the OH, while the reactive hydrogen atoms are available for doing chemical work. They will combine with any suitable hydrogen acceptor. In the plant they are used chiefly to combine with a coenzyme (DPNH)[1] which is used to transfer

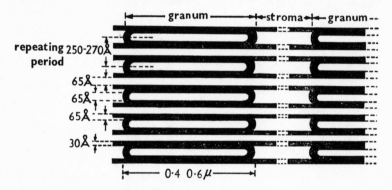

FIG. 17. Part of section through a chloroplast showing the lamellae (Steinmann and Sjöstrand)

the hydrogen to form energy-rich compounds. It has been suggested that the function of the membranes in the protoplast is to keep H and OH apart from each other so that they do not recombine.

The overall reaction is to take carbon dioxide from the atmosphere and 'reduce' it by the addition of hydrogen and the removal of oxygen, so that it can be converted into carbohydrates. The course of this reaction has been worked by Calvin and his associates by the use of carbon dioxide labelled with radioactive carbon. They find that the carbon dioxide enters into a complicated cycle of changes. It is taken in at one stage of this cycle and the product is reduced to a sugar-like compound by the DPNH, which has been formed from hydrogen atoms under the action of light in the protoplast.

The main result of these researches was to show that the formation of sugars and other carbohydrates is not a simple direct process,

[1] Diphosphopyridine nucleotide, hydrogenated.

but one which occurs in a number of stages. This is probably an advantage from the plant's point of view because it has to make large numbers of other compounds besides carbohydrates and the intermediates of the carbon dioxide-sugar process are also available for carrying out many other necessary reactions. It is interesting to find that the basic process of photosynthesis is the splitting of water (H_2O) into H and OH, and the use of the reactive hydrogen atoms to bring about reactions which result in the production of energy-rich compounds, on which all animal life depends.

Since all life still depends on photosynthesis, it is impossible not to conclude that the earliest manifestations of life made use of the energy of radiation. As we have seen, the ionizing radiations produce highly reactive species of molecules directly and it is quite possible that at the beginning the process which led to living things used the more penetrating radiations. But in the photosynthetic mechanism of the living plant, a means has been found of using the much gentler visible radiations of light, which are harnessed in the mechanism of the chloroplast. This is effected by the chlorophyll molecules which can absorb visible light and use it to split water. The chlorophyll system acts as an energy transformer, and a very efficient one, for the conversion of light into chemical energy.

Theoretically the energy of at least three photons of visible light[1] should be required to turn one molecule of carbon dioxide into carbohydrate. Many measurements have been made to determine the number actually required in living cells. The results are rather variable owing to the extremely variable circumstances which obtain; but under good conditions a value of eight photons per molecule has been observed. This indicates that the efficiency of the photosynthetic apparatus in converting light energy under the best conditions is at least 35 per cent.

The amount of solar radiation falling on the earth is quite enormous. For example, in the United States, on the average 1,000 calories reach each square foot of land during the daytime every minute.[2] For an acre of land this equivalent to the output of an electrical station generating 2,600,000 kilowatts! About half of this is made up of heat rays not available for photosynthesis. The total amount of energy which could actually be used for photosynthesis under the best possible conditions is thus about $\frac{1}{2} \times 35$ per cent $\times$ 1,000 = 175 calories per sq foot per minute or $3{\cdot}85 \times 10^9$ calories

---

[1] The photon is hv where h is the Planck constant and v the frequency of the light. *hv* varies from 40 to 70 kcals. per molecule according to the wavelength of the visible light.

[2] This is enough to heat 1 litre of water 1°C.

per acre per day of nine hours' sunshine. This would be sufficient to produce about one ton of carbohydrate material from carbon dioxide, on the basis of the best efficiency which is reached in laboratory experiments. Actual agricultural operations do not approach this degree of efficiency. The average yield of agricultural production is not more than two tons per acre per year,[1] which is clearly very much less than the optimum obtainable from a plant under ideal conditions. There are of course many reasons why only a small fraction of the photosynthetic energy of sunshine is actually utilized in practice, but it is clear that in sunshine, particularly in the tropics, we have a source of energy and of synthesis far exceeding all other sources, such as coal, oil and atomic energy, and the photosynthetic apparatus of green cells is remarkably well adapted to its utilization to make a host of compounds.

[1] The data given here are taken from an article by F. Daniels in *Hollænder's Radiation Biology*, Vol. III.

Specialized Cells: Muscles, Nerves and Sense Organs

꒰ꙮ꒱

It is difficult to convey any idea of the extraordinary variety of cells in the animal organism. Besides those already mentioned there are, for example, cells which lay down the bones of the skeleton in the young animal; the cells which produce hair and nails, which in many cases continue to function for the whole of life; and the mammary cells of the female which, after the birth of young, produce large quantities of milk. The latter are a veritable factory of proteins, fats and other constituents. Here is a description by Professor H. D. Kay of the operation of the milk-producing cells of the cow. 'The day's work of one of these cubical cells entails the following cycle of operations. It begins as a rather squat cell with the nucleus in the middle. Granules or globules, some of which stain with fat soluble dyes, then begin to appear in the part of the cell nearest the alveolar space. The cell begins to increase in length and size, the nucleus remaining close to the basement membrane. The secretory products soon fill the whole of one end of the tall distended cell. These products, and possibly a small part of the cytoplasm of the cell itself, are now extruded into the lumen as milk, following which discharge the cell returns to its original squat shape. This whole process is repeated several times. . . . During the twenty-four hours in an actively lactating cow there may be up to four or five, or even more cycles of operation. . . .'

However, perhaps the most interesting cells are those which give the animal the power of movement and those which enable him to become aware of the nature of his environment. These cells, which form muscles and sense organs and nerves are so important in the higher manifestations of life, that we must look at them in some detail. They have to be taken together because, as a rule, the operation of one involves the functioning of at least one of the other two.

MUSCLE

The simplest organs which produce motion are the flagella or streamers attached to some bacteria (Fig. 18). These seem to be threads or filaments of protein. They are capable of swaying from side to side in a kind of wave motion and this propels the bacterium through the water. Spermatozoa have a similar organ in their tails which enables them to swim through the vaginal fluid until they reach the ovum. These tails contain the enzymes which are required to produce the energy they need from the breakdown of sugar—they are in fact miniature muscles. However, it is likely that they start their journey with a supply of 'fuel', i.e. sugar, and when this is used up they are unable to go any further.

The muscles of the higher animals are large masses of cells which

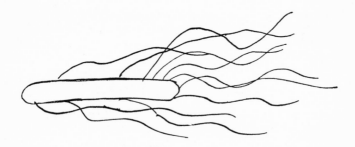

FIG. 18. A bacterium with flagellae (*B. proteus vulg.*, after Weibull)

have the power of contracting. They are often attached to the bones of the skeleton by tendons and are able to exert considerable forces.

Muscle is clearly a very complicated organ and it has been studied from several points of view. These concern themselves with different parts of the whole question; they are all necessary and a complete explanation of muscle action must cover the three main problems to which an answer is required. These are:

(1) The mechanical arrangements whereby contraction occurs;
(2) the biochemical reactions which provide the energy;
(3) the 'activation process', usually stimulated by nerve signals, which causes the muscle to contract.

All these have been exhaustively studied and at different times the emphasis has been put mainly on one or the other. For a long period (1920-1940) much of the interest was in the biochemical reactions which provided the energy of muscular contraction and these have been fairly fully worked out. It has been established that the energy-providing mechanism is not greatly different to that of other cells (see p. 47) and that the energy produced by the oxidation of sugar becomes available to the muscle in the form of the adenosine triphosphate (ATP)—another example of how the biochemical mechanisms are closely related to each other, since the same basic energy yielding cycle is used both for protein and nucleic acid synthesis and for giving the energy required by the muscles.

The chemical composition of muscle has also been studied for a long time. Kühne in 1864 extracted a soluble protein called myosin. Nearly eighty years later, Straub in the laboratory of Szent-Györgyi found another component in muscle which he called actin. The compound of actin and myosin (actomyosin) had marked contractile properties, and as myosin itself was found to be a powerful agent for decomposing ATP and as the latter caused the contraction of synthetic actomyosin threads, it appeared that the most important agents in the muscle mechanism had been isolated.

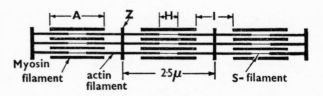

FIG. 19. Structure of striated muscle fibres (Huxley)

More recently attention has been given to the structure of the fibres in the intact muscle. The existence of striations or banding in many muscle fibres had been observed by microscopists during the nineteenth century. The striations consist of alternate zones having higher and lower refractive index and were sometimes called dark and light bands. The spacing of the bands is about 2.5μ, i.e. between 1/100 and 1/1000 of a millimetre. Their existence has been confirmed by electron microscope pictures of thin sections of muscle (see Plate 14). Numerous attempts have been made to identify the substances present in the bands by dissolving out the different components separately. Finally, Dr H. E. Huxley and Miss Hanson on one hand and Drs A. F. Huxley and R. Niedergerke both proposed in 1954, on the bases of their observations, the picture shown in Fig. 19.

The continuous threads running through the muscles are actin filaments, which are held together at intervals by a kind of spacing plate (the Z line). The myosin filaments run side by side with these, but

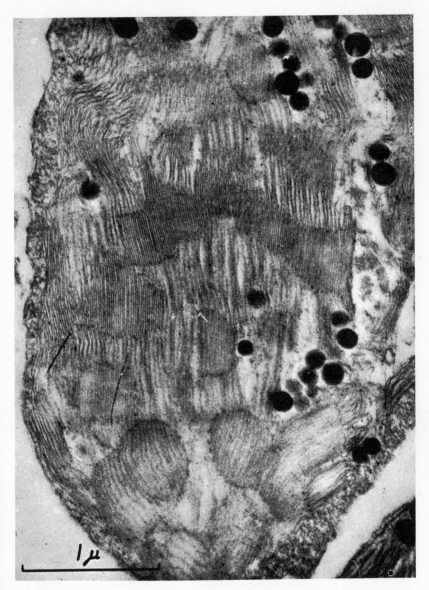

13 A cross section of a chloroplast from *Aspidistra elatior*. (Reproduced by permission from Steinmann and Sjöstrand, *Experimental Cell Research*, 8, 15, 1955.)

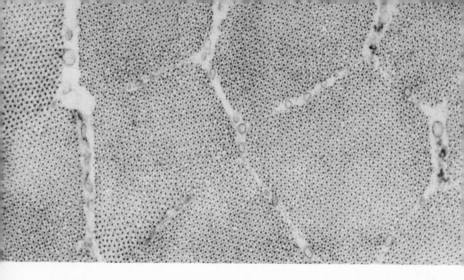

14 Electron micrographs of muscle fibrils. The upper picture is a section across the main direction of the fibril. The larger circles are the myosin filaments and the small points are the actin filaments. The lower picture is a longitudinal section which shows the various bands described in the text. These photographs are reproduced by permission of Dr H. E. Huxley

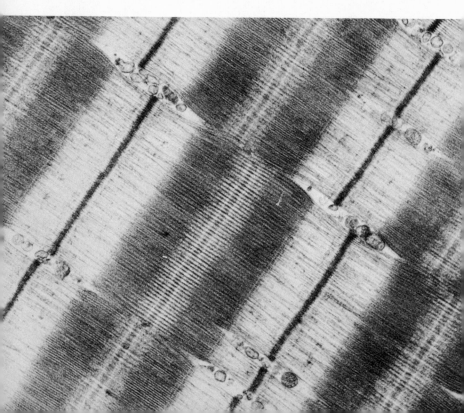

they do not occupy the whole space between the Z lines. When the muscle shortens, the two kinds of filaments of actin and myosin respectively, *slide past* each other. The actin filaments do not themselves shorten when the muscle contracts, but there is in the middle region between two Z lines a filament which is very contractible. It thus holds two rather rigid actin rods together and permits them to slide through the spaces between the myosin rods.

According to this structure, which is now fairly well supported by

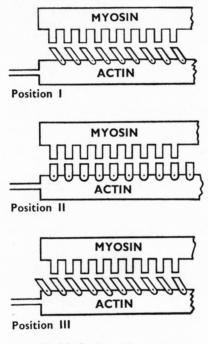

FIG. 20. Mechanism of contraction in muscle fibres

numerous observations, the contraction of muscle is due to the sliding of myosin and actin fibres alongside each other. Much less is known about this aspect of the mechanism. It is certain that ATP must be involved in this process as the source of energy; but the way in which it operates is uncertain, although various possible processes have been suggested. It is likely that the two filaments move with respect to each other, by attachments between them which are broken in one way and remade in another. Thus the one filament may move along

H

the other by a centipede kind of motion (Fig. 20). The ATP would be involved either in the making or the breaking of attachments and the energy required would be provided in some way by the energy rich bonds of the ATP. Fig. 20 is a rather fanciful picture of such a process.

The final question we must ask is how the muscle is activated, i.e. what causes it to begin to contract. As a general rule, as we shall see, muscle action is excited or initiated by electrical disturbances arriving down a nerve. This excitation causes the movement of inorganic ions across the membrane in which the muscle fibres are enclosed. There is a special region of the muscle fibre surface which is in contact with the nerve and it is here that the processes leading to excitement take place. It was shown by Sir Henry Dale and Prof G. L. Brown that, when the nerve signal arrives in this region, the substance acetylcholine is liberated. It was also found that an enzyme capable of destroying acetylcholine is also present; so that the acetylcholine formed only lasts for a short time. The idea that the actual process of muscle excitation is brought about by acetylcholine has been confirmed by two facts: (1) substances which inhibit acetylcholine action interfere with the excitation of the muscle, (2) acetylcholine, when applied artificially, does give rise to muscle contractions. However, very little is known about how the electrical disturbance arriving along the muscle causes the release of acetylcholine, and not a great deal is known of the changes which acetylcholine brings about, except that it causes marked changes in the ease with which sodium and potassium ions can penetrate the muscle membrane.

SENSE ORGANS

Sensitiveness to the environment is probably a fundamental property of living cells. Even the most primitive forms of life respond to some degree to heat or cold, to light and to chemical substances. Sensitiveness to light is probably a part of the original character of life, since as we have seen, the original living complex must have been photosensitive and able to use light energy. Sensitiveness to chemical compounds must also be a very primitive feature of life, since many chemicals upset the delicate balance of the life processes and, in fact, many products of enzyme action are themselves inhibitors and prevent enzymes working properly. Organisms often cannot live unless the substances they produce are removed. They also need a fresh supply of the substances used for food and can often detect them at appreciable distances, e.g. the whelk can detect the compounds formed by decaying animal matter at a considerable distance.

Many primitive animals are light sensitive to some extent over the whole surface. Others, such as starfishes, have specially sensitive eye spots, and illumination brings about movement either towards or away from the light.[1]

Out of these primitive responses, living things have developed during the ages the most astonishing sense organs. In a world in which the competition for food was severe, the possession of even slightly more effective means of finding it must have had great survival value. It is not surprising that the struggle for existence has produced a steady improvement until the beautiful arrangements possessed by the higher animals at the present time were elaborated. Special cells have been developed which have in many cases a most extraordinary sensitiveness to particular kinds of stimulus. The olfactory cells of the nose of some animals is capable of detecting extremely small quantities of some chemical compounds. It is well known that dogs can follow a human being by smell the day after he has gone along the track. It has been demonstrated that in the nose of the dog a single molecule of a fatty acid must be capable of stimulating the smell organ.[2]

Insects also have an extraordinary smell ability. Female gypsy moths can, it is said, attract the male from distances up to two miles by means of an odour. The male will respond to the excised scent gland of the female or even to a piece of blotting paper which has been touched by the scent gland but if the antennae of the males are removed, they are quite unresponsive. Parasitic wasps can locate their larval hosts, even when buried several centimetres in wood.

The human eye is a most fantastic example of fitness and efficiency. It is incredibly complicated. The retina of each eye contains about 120 million sensitive elements in the form of rods and about 6 million cones. About a million nerve fibres take their responses to stimulation into the brain. It is obvious that many of these sensitive elements must share a single nerve fibre.

The purpose of this arrangement is to provide both night and day vision. The rods, which provide for night vision, are extremely sensitive and many of them share a single nerve fibre. This means that the nerve fibre has a large number of terminations, which are spread out so as to catch all the available light. It has been shown by Dr M. H. Pirenne that the sensitiveness of the eye approaches the maximum possible, which could be reached if every quantum of light impinging on the retina produced a sensation. Careful measurements by Pirenne

---

[1] N. Millott, 'Animal Photosensitivity', *Endeavour*, XVI, 19, 1957.
[2] One molecule of the fatty acid, when applied to about 10^4 sense cells, can be detected. The chance of two molecules reaching one cell in the smell organ under these circumstances is remote.

have shown that at the limit of detection, not more than a very few quanta are actually absorbed in the rods in order to produce a detectable sensation of light. Because one nerve serves an appreciable area, this kind of vision is not very sharp.

The cones which sometimes have an optic nerve to themselves and sometimes share an optic nerve in groups of two or three, provide for a sharply discriminating kind of vision under conditions of good illumination. They are also sensitive to different kinds of light, as they are responsible for colour vision.

What does light do when it reaches the retina? It is absorbed by a pigment called visual purple or rhodopsin, which can easily be extracted from the eyes of animals and has been much studied in recent years by R. A. Morton in Liverpool and by G. Wald in Harvard. It has been found to be a protein combined with a special light absorbing molecule. The latter is a near relative of Vitamin A— thus explaining why deficiency of Vitamin A leads to night blindness. Different animals make use of slightly different derivatives of Vitamin A; beef rhodopsin uses Vitamin A_1 and fish rhodopsin the slightly different Vitamin A_2. These molecules all have a row of alternating single and double bonds, which give them their light absorbing property. Molecules of this kind have one electron for each carbon atom, called a π-electron, which is in a special state. Instead of being anchored to one carbon atom as the others are, it is free to wander up and down the carbon chain. The effect of the absorption of light is to activate the π-electrons, so that they take up the energy of the light absorbed and acquire a state of high energy in which they are able to escape from the light absorbing molecule into the protein it is attached to. This results in the bleaching of the dye. Dr Wald has described this change as follows: 'When rhodopsin is exposed to light in the retina, two major changes occur, the carotinoid (the dye molecule) is cleaved from the protein and is degraded through orange intermediates, first to orange retinene 1, and then to colourless

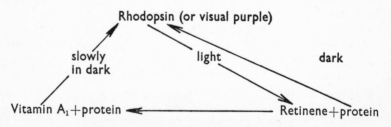

Retinene is the 'aldehyde' of Vitamin A

Vitamin A_1. The retina can also resynthesize rhodopsin in two ways, first from retinene, and relatively slowly from Vitamin A_1.'

What happens when the protein of rhodopsin receives the liberated electron is not clearly known, but the final result is to stimulate the optic nerve, so that electrical disturbances pass down it to the brain. This can be demonstrated by experiments, in which an electrode is placed in contact with the optic nerve of the frog. Whenever light falls on the retina an electrical disturbance passes down the nerve, which can be detected by means of the electrode and if an amplifier is put into the circuit with a loud speaker, the result of the passage of the electric impulse is a click in the loud speaker. It appears from these experiments that the frog responds to changes in the intensity of light, i.e. when the light is turned on or off, but steady illumination produces no further response. However in man and probably other mammals steady illumination causes a continuous stimulation of the nerves.

NERVES

This brings us to the links between the sensory organs and the muscles. Usually this is *via* the brain—a sort of clearing house for the information coming from the senses; but this will require several chapters by itself. For the moment we will look at the nerves themselves, white threads of many different sizes and lengths; sometimes in bundles, sometimes singly, which traverse the body like a telephone system.

For many years scientists have wondered how these messages are transmitted. Even Newton speculated on this and thought that it was a purely mechanical transmission of a mechanical impulse. To Descartes what was transmitted was 'like a very subtle wind . . . continually mounting in great abundance from the heart to the brain, flows from there through the nerves to the muscles, and gives motion to the members'.

According to this the nerves were just tubes which permitted the flow of 'animal spirits'. It was L. Galvani who showed that the flow was electrical, and analogous to the electric discharges obtainable from static electric machines which were common at this time. He showed that frog's muscles could be made to contract by electric currents applied to the nerve of the spinal column. 'Animal spirits' thus became 'animal electricity' which was supposed to be secreted by the brain and travelled along the nerves.

Many years of research have confirmed the electrical nature of the impulses which pass down the nerve fibres. This can easily be demonstrated by putting electrodes on two parts of an exposed nerve and connecting them to an electrometer. These impulses can even be detected outside the body using the sensitive electronic amplifiers now available, yet it has been found that the analogy with electric currents in metallic conductors is not at all close. The nerve fibres themselves are rather complicated structures. When examined in the living state, or recently excised, they consist of long cylindrical threads, usually 2-20μ in diameter, although much larger ones are sometimes found. Every nerve has grown out of a nerve cell and as a kind of extension of it (Plate 15). Each fibre of a typical nerve con-

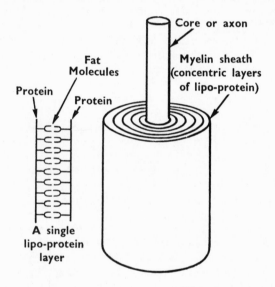

FIG. 21. A nerve with myelin sheath

sists of a 'core' or axon, which is enclosed in a membrane. In the case of 'myelinated' nerves, the core is covered by a glistening sheath of a white substance called myelin which has been shown by electron microscope pictures to consist of a large number of concentric layers of material. This material is a combination of protein with a fatty substance, which together constitute a 'lipo-protein'. It has been found that the molecules of the fat are enclosed between thin layers of protein and the long hydrocarbon chains of the fatty substance are arranged with their lengths pointing outwards from the centre of the fibre (see Fig. 21). Inside this myelin sheath is a soft jelly-like substance consisting of proteins and inorganic salts which is in fact continuous with the cytoplasm of the nerve cell, and contains mitochondria and other particles necessary to maintain the life of the cell (Plate 15).

During recent years many experiments have been made, especially by A. L. Hodgkin and A. F. Huxley, using the giant nerve fibres of the squid, which are so large (0·5 mm. or more in diameter) that it is possible to put electrodes under the axon jelly and so detect the changes which occur when the nerve impulse passes. These fibres are not myelinated, but they do possess a lipo-protein covering, which plays a very important part in the action. The composition of the fluid inside the fibre is very different to that of the blood plasma in which is usually immersed (see Fig. 22). In fact, while the blood plasma contains about twenty times as much sodium (Na) as potassium (K) the interior of the fibre contains ten times as much potassium as sodium. There is also a marked difference between the concentrations of chloride (Cl) ions inside and outside.

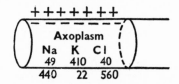

FIG. 22. Distribution of inorganic ions inside and outside the nerve fibre

These differences persist in an unexcited fibre because although potassium can pass freely through the membrane, sodium cannot and there is also an efficient mechanism (a sodium pump) for removing sodium from inside the membrane when its concentration is too high.

Because of the inequalities in the amounts of the sodium, potassium and chloride (which are present as electrically charged ions) inside and outside the fibre, there is a difference of electrical potential across the fibre membrane and as a result the outside has a positive charge and the inside a negative charge. (Fig. 22.)

When a nerve impulse passes down the fibre, the permeability of the membrane to sodium ions is momentarily increased. As they are at a higher concentration outside, they immediately pass through into the interior, and as a consequence the negative charge on the inner surface is reduced and it may be reversed. (Fig. 23.)

When the impulse has passed, the membrane properties are restored. The excess of sodium ions which has reached the inside of the fibre is pumped out again and some potassium ions also escape so that the original condition of the charges on the membrane is restored.

The nervous impulse is thus a transitory disturbance in the electrical condition of the nerve membrane which travels along the nerve. A single disturbance of this kind takes as a rule a few thousandths of a second to pass any point on the fibre. Its speed down the fibre is

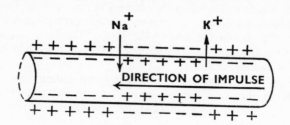

FIG. 23. How the electric impulse passes down the nerve fibre

comparatively low, depending on the diameter of the fibre (about twenty metres a second in the giant squid nerves). This speed is of course very much less than the normal speed of electric conduction processes (which may approach the speed of light). It is determined by the rates of the various processes by which the impulse is transmitted.

Much remains to be learnt about the nervous impulse, and about how it is started and how it acts when it reaches its destination in the muscle. It seems a rather unpromising mechanism for precise control of muscle action. We could hardly have anticipated from what we know of its mechanism that such a process should have been capable of such an extraordinary degree of elaboration so that it eventually became the basis of mentality.

XV

The Brain and What It Does

꽁

Now we come to one of the largest collections of cells in the animal body, the brain. In man, it consists of a mass of nerve cells or neurones, at least 12,000 million of them, connected together by very numerous branching nerve-like threads, of which the largest are called axons (see Plate 15). Into it go most of the nerves coming from the sense organs and out of it come many of the nerves which control the muscles. We could say that the brain is like a telephone exchange in which the proper circuits are connected together, but this does not help very much in explaining how the information provided by the senses is organized and made use of, and how complicated muscle actions are controlled.

We can easily recognize a number of different ways by which muscles can be put into action. The simplest way is the involuntary reflex action in which a sensation brings about an automatic involuntary response, like the contraction of the iris when a bright light is shone before the eye, or the sudden withdrawal of the hand if a needle is pushed into it. These reflex actions often scarcely involve the brain at all; they occur in animals in which at least the higher parts of the brain have been removed. Similar to these are responses which control automatic muscular rhythms, like the beating of the heart, where one stage of the rhythmic process, when it is completed automatically, initiates the next. Other processes, like breathing, are semi-automatic. They normally look after themselves, but we can interfere with them if we want to.

Something is known about the ways in which such automatic or semi-automatic actions are controlled. The muscles themselves are provided with sensory nerves which send out messages indicating their state of contraction. This was discovered by Sir Charles Bell as long ago as 1826. In a famous paper, which he presented to the

Royal Society, he said:

'We are sensible of the most minute changes of muscular exertion, by which we know the position of the body and limbs, when there is no other means of knowledge open to us. If a rope-dancer measures her steps by the eye, yet on the other hand a blind man can balance his body. In study, walking and running, every effort of the voluntary power, which gives motion to the body, is directed by a sense of the condition of the muscles and without this sense they could not regulate their actions.'

He showed that the muscles are provided with sensory nerves, which send out messages indicating their state of contraction and in other ways also indicate what have been the results of the muscle contractions. These messages reach the brain so that 'between the brain and the muscles there is a circle of nerves; one nerve conveys the influence from the brain to the muscle, and this gives the sense of the condition of the muscle to the brain'. (Fig. 24.)

This method of control is quite common in machines, which are often provided with governors or speed controllers, arranged so that the output of the machine controls the power which is supplied to it, i.e. the input. A good example is the governor of a steam engine,

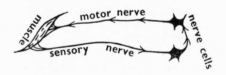

FIG. 24. The nervous circle

which closes a valve when the pressure exceeds a critical value.

The flow of water through a pipe can be kept constant by making the outflowing water partly close a valve in the inflow when the outflow speed is too great. Electric motors can easily be arranged with speed controls which cut down the operating current when the speed is too high. The general principle is known as 'feedback', i.e. some of the output is used to control the input.

The same principle is used in controlling the muscles. The impulses received from the sensory nerves stimulate or inhibit the impulses sent out by the motor nerves, and this controls whether the muscle will be stimulated to contract or not stimulated. If the sensory nerve is cut the muscle is as completely paralysed as if the motor nerve is cut. In this way the muscle is kept in a constant state of tension which is required to do the work it has to do.

Similar and probably much simpler involuntary responses to stimuli are quite common even in very primitive kinds of animals. Some organisms will move towards the light, others will move into shaded regions. For example, some hydrozoa, like *Gonionemus*, prefer to be in the shaded parts of an illuminated tank; others, such as *Englena viridis*, seek the lighted parts. The mollusc, *Pholas*, in which the whole surface is said to be light sensitive, retracts its syphon in response to light, while in *Ciona intestinalis*, light causes a closure of the syphon apertures. In sea urchins the spines react to variations in light, e.g. in *Diadema antillarum*, spines are moved vigorously towards regions shaded by objects.[1]

Worms like *Branchiomma* have light-sensitive tentacles, and the passage of a shadow over these tentacles causes it to withdraw into its tube. Starfish often have light-sensitive patches (or primitive eye-spots) on the tips of the rays.

Many organisms react to the presence of chemical substances, like oxygen. These are all automatic responses to stimulation which act directly on the organism's means of propulsion.

But in all the more developed forms of animal life, something more than simple reflex action is required. The animal must not only receive sense impressions; in order to make use of them, it must be able to make some sort of an interpretation of them. The interpretation is based on experience, i.e. on the results of previous actions in similar situations. The animal learns from experience, and he could not learn if he did not remember.

This is an entirely new thing in the world of life; a totally different mode of response to stimulation and one which has turned out to be enormously more effective. It is, in fact, the first beginnings of mentality since the animal learns something about his surroundings and uses, or tries to make use of, that knowledge.

Very many experiments have been made of this learning process. Professor J. Z. Young has experimented with octopuses. They were offered either a crab or a crab with a white plate behind it. The animal lived among some bricks at one end of a tank and the crab was lowered by a thread at the other end. As soon as the moving crab appears, the octopus swims or walks across the tank and throws itself over the crab, gathers it up and returns with it to its home. When the crab with the white plate was presented, an electric shock was applied as soon as the octopus had seized the crab. This caused it to go back to its home quite quickly and it very soon learnt to associate this unpleasant experience with the white plate so that,

[1] N. Millott, *Endeavour*, XVI, 19 (1957).

when the crab and plate are presented, it merely 'leans forward from its home and watches the situation'.[1]

The most famous experiments were, however, those of Pavlov. If a hungry dog is shown food, its mouth begins to water. It is obvious that the sensation given by the sight and smell of the food in some way causes the salivary glands to excrete. This is a simple reflex action, and the salivation is an involuntary response. If a bell is rung before the food is shown, the animal will associate the sound of the bell with food and the sound of the bell will, for a time, cause his mouth to water. This is a *conditioned reflex*. It is obvious that connections have been established in the brain between messages arriving from the eyes or nose and the ear, in such a way that a message received by the ear stimulates a response which is normally produced by ear and nose messages.

The conditioned reflex was regarded by Dr J. B. Watson and the behaviourist school of psychology as a sufficient explanation of nearly the whole of animal behaviour. They regarded *all* responses of the individual animal to environment as either direct (like the knee jerk) or somewhat modified by recollections of previous situations which might cause the simplest response to be delayed or inhibited; or 'conditioned' by circumstances indirectly connected with them (like the sound of Pavlov's bell).

But in fact the 'conditioned reflex' is itself a very complicated phenomenon and the existence of many of the profounder abilities of the brain are implied in it. As I said, it obviously requires the existence of memory of past experiences and the ability to interpret present experiences in the light of past, and therefore the ability to learn from experience.

These must be discussed in detail; but in the first place it will be helpful to have a clearer idea of the actual organization in the brain, and some notion of how it handles the messages it receives from the senses.

BRAIN ACTIVITY

The brain of a large animal, as I have said, consists of an enormous mass of neurones. Some distinct parts can be demonstrated; the cerebellum, which is largely concerned with the more 'animal' functions such as balance and the posture of the body, and the cerebrum, which is covered by the cerebral cortex, which reaches its greatest development in man, a great convoluted membrane, about a hundred

[1] B. B. Boycott and J. Z. Young. S.E.B. Symposium on Physiological Mechanisms of Animal Behaviour (1950), p. 432.

neurones deep, the so-called grey matter of the brain (to distinguish it from the underlying white matter). The cerebrum in man contains 9,000 million cells, out of the 12,000 million present in the whole brain.

Our knowledge of what goes on in the brain is rather meagre. There is undoubtedly a great deal of electrical activity going on. As we have seen, it is possible, if a nerve fibre is laid bare, to detect the passage of an electrical impulse or wave by placing electrodes at two different points along it.

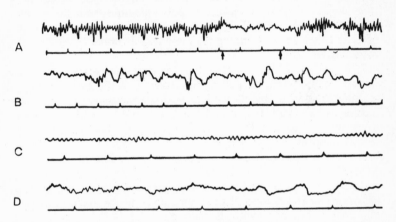

FIG. 25. Electroencephalograph patterns of brain activity recorded through the skulls of human beings (the regular marks below the tracings are time signals at 1 second intervals).
  A. A normal subject. The eyes were closed between the two arrows on the time line
  B. A subject who has had a brain injury. The sharp downward spikes are very characteristic of certain kinds of injury
  C. A normal subject (the oscillations are less magnified vertically than in A)
  D. Same subject as C, in sleep induced by a drug
(Reproduced by courtesy of Dr W. F. Floyd, Middlesex Hospital Medical School)

These electrical impulses can also be detected outside the brain by electrodes placed on the skin at different points. With a delicate electronic amplifier called an electro-encephalograph, it is then possible to detect oscillations or surges of electric action within the brain (Fig. 25). These surges must occur on a rather large scale, i.e. to produce an effect outside the skull many of the electric circuits of the brain must be oscillating in unison. So far it has been difficult to connect these oscillations very closely with the mental state of the individual being examined, except that in epileptics sharp spikes are observed. They may only be a kind of 'carrier wave' on which the actual messages are superimposed. We are like strangers outside a great power station; we hear faintly the hum of activity going on inside it, but we do not know what it means. We do know that the oscillations are larger and more clearly defined when we are awake and giving attention, and give way to a long, slow rhythm when we are asleep.

More detailed information has been obtained by experiments with animals. By means of electrodes placed on the optic nerves of a frog, we can detect the electric impulses coming from the excited nerve cells in the retina. They can be traced a little way into the brain itself and then are lost among the innumerable fibres which join the neurones.

It is also possible to locate the region of the cortex which the signals finally reach, by putting electrodes into the exposed brains of patients and also by electro-encephalograph records taken on the outside of the skull. It is found that the impulses produced by the retina are spread over a great area of the brain. The picture on the retina is enormously magnified and it would appear that millions of brain cells are concerned with the vision of one instant.

The brain of an animal, and especially human beings, is thus primarily an instrument for co-ordinating large numbers of separate impressions. The *pattern* of the impressions means much more than the separate bits of which it is made up.

When we look at a half-tone picture in a newspaper, we no doubt see the separate dots. but we are only interested in the pattern of light and shade which they make. The brain has a remarkable power of finding the pattern in millions of diverse sense impressions and there must be something basic and inherent in its structure which permits it to do this If it is more concerned with the pattern of the diverse sense impressions than with the details of the individual impressions, it must follow that the interrelations between the brain cells which receive the impressions are more important than the actual impression made on each one.

If we look at a square, it is the fact that it is a particular kind of geometrical figure that we seize upon. We are indifferent to its size. The actual size of the image on our retina depends on our distance from the object. The projection of the square in our brain thus depends on our distance from it—yet we have no difficulty in recognizing it as the same square. It is clear that in interpreting very simple experiences, the brain has to make very complicated adjustments. However, you can only find a pattern in your sensory impressions by recognizing something you have seen before. You could not recognize objects as squares unless you had previously seen and made a note of this feature. So picking out the features of a pattern and recognizing them involves memory and also to some extent learning about them. So we see that we do not *spontaneously* interpret our sense impressions. The use we make depends on our memory of similar experiences and the meanings we have found in them.

MEMORY

There is every reason to think that the stimulation of brain cells leaves a permanent trace of some kind. This is not very surprising, as all living cells are to some extent influenced permanently by external agencies acting on them. The state of a cell at any one moment depends on what has happened before and everyone who has worked even with simple organisms such as bacteria knows how hard it is to reproduce a particular condition exactly. This amounts to saying that all living cells have some kind of a memory of what has happened to them, so that it is not surprising to find, perhaps to a much more highly developed degree, that brain cells are permanently influenced by the sensory images they received. But the exact nature of the memory record, whether it is proved by changes in molecules or structures, or whether permanently circulating currents of electricity are set up, is hardly known.

The memory record made by the brain must, however, have one characteristic if it is to be of any use. It must be available for inspection. It is no use having a gramophone record unless we can play it. So our memory impressions will be useless unless they can at least be used for recognition. There must be some way of comparing the sensation of the moment, with what is remembered of previous sensations. Exactly how this is done is not known. We might think that the sense impressions circulate among the cells until they find something with which they correspond—holes into which they fit. Alternatively it is possible that the memory record is able to send out again, perhaps rather weakly, a copy or repetition of the electrical impulses which caused it—so that we could have a direct comparison between the fresh impulses arriving from the senses and the fainter images coming from the memory record.

DEALING WITH SENSE IMPRESSIONS

It will be obvious from this that the reception of a sense impression in the brain is not an isolated act, but something which is part of a continuing process—in fact of something which has been going on since birth. The new sense impressions just take their place as a continuation of a long series and the interpretation which is found in them depends on what has been learnt about the previous experiences.

This means that the memory record is not a static thing—something finished and done with. It is like a message on a long tape, on which fresh signals are appearing all the time. But there is a vital difference from a tape message. The messages which arrive in the brain are co-ordinated and compared with previous part of the record. We recognize this feature or that feature—in fact the meaning of the sense impression is determined entirely by this comparison with previous experiences and by the interpretations which we are able to make as a result.

Our experience at any one moment is thus a combination of the sense images of the moment with memories of the past, and it is difficult to separate the one from the other. This characteristic, i.e. that sense impressions are interpreted in terms of the meaning which has been found in previous experiences, seems to be a fundamental ability of the human brain and probably also to a less extent of that of the higher animals. The relative importance of that part coming from the sense and that coming from the memory may vary very greatly. But something of this kind seems to be a necessity where behaviour is to be determined both by the present situation and by what has been learnt from past experiences.

So far we have been thinking of the impressions reaching the senses in a rather simple way. We have actually tried to isolate rather simple sense impressions and see how they are dealt with. But in practice we are receiving all the time a multitude of sense impressions, some important and some unimportant. How do we manage to sort them out?

It is clear that, out of the multitudinous sense impressions that pour in on us, we are able to produce a consistent picture, which includes the most important elements of the situation which need concern us. This picture necessarily involves discrimination between the important and unimportant; it necessarily concerns itself with the broad outlines and not with every detail of the sense impressions. It is to a great extent built up by recognizing features we are familiar with. Thus one glance at an object is sufficient for us to recognize it as a table. We do not have to study it carefully and try to make up our minds whether it is really a camel or an ant-hill.

So we see that our sense impressions are not used at first hand; it is the interpretations which we are able to make of them which are

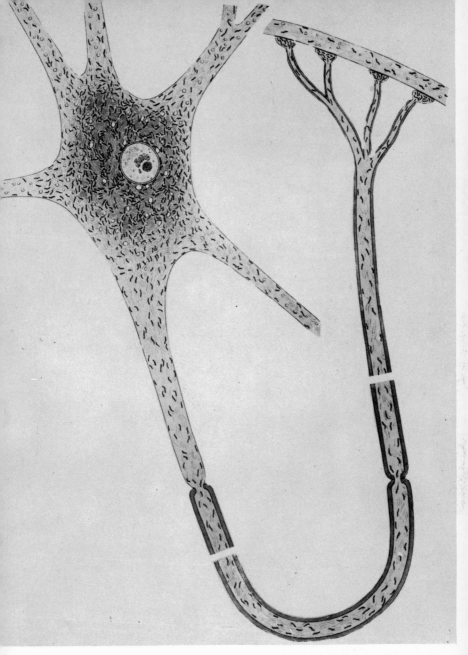

15 A nerve cell of the mammalian spinal chord and the associated nerve fibre. This is not a photograph but a diagrammatic representation which shows the principal features. The little black 'worms' are mitochondria and the grey ones are microsomes. The open circles are fat-bearing particles. (From an article by J. Z. Young, *Endeavour*, 15, 5, 1956, reproduced by permission.)

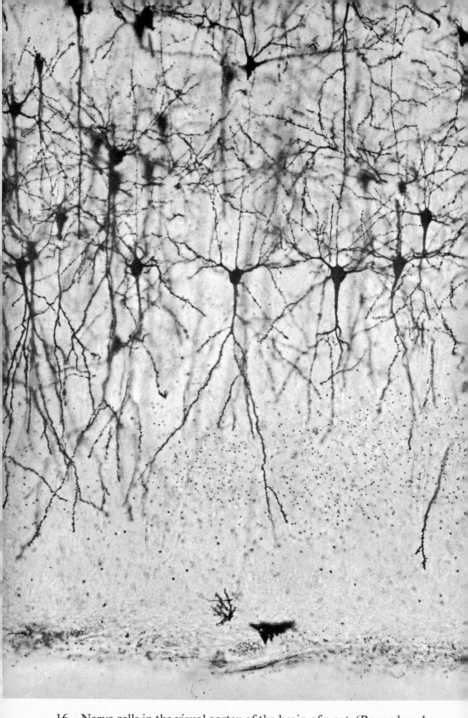

16   Nerve cells in the visual cortex of the brain of a cat. (Reproduced by permission of Dr D. A. Sholl and Methuen and Co. from *The Cerebral Cortex*)

useful. It follows from this that besides the regions in the brain which are able to *register* sensations, there must be those which are capable of finding significant patterns in the sensations as they are received, which are concerned with the meaning and interpretation of the sense pictures of the moment. It is quite likely that at this stage much of the detail is lost. Also the actual size and orientation of the object becomes of less importance. We recognize an object as the same at different distances, although the area it occupies on the retina may be quite different. We recognize a particular shape such as a square whatever its size. This means that the recognition occurs at a level where the actual size is unimportant, only the pattern is significant. We have very little idea how this is effected in the brain.

It might be natural to expect that this process of finding meanings takes place in the cerebral cortex. It is surprising, however, how much damage can be done to the brain without apparently impairing its functions. A hundred years ago a quarryman in Vermont, Phineas Gage, had a crowbar driven through his skull, causing an ugly wound in both of the frontal lobes of the brain. By good luck the wound healed and the man was able to return to work. His intelligence and ability were not seriously impaired and his memory was good; however, he was said to be less balanced and more easily excited to anger.

An operation known as prefrontal lobotomy or leucotomy, in which many of the nerve connections between the frontal lobes are severed, has been performed on a considerable number of people with mental derangements. It appears to have a genuine effect on the tendency of the patient to worry, but it does not radically affect his memory.

From this it would seem that a considerable number of nerve connections in the brain can be broken without seriously affecting the memory or the general ability of the person, although it may be that some of the more general abilities, which we call judgment and character, may be lost.

A possible reason for this is that the total number of possible paths between the nerve cells is so enormous that only a small proportion of them is actually used. When some paths are broken, alternative ones are available. Another conceivable explanation is that the number of nerve cells is very much greater than is actually required, or at least greater than the number made use of. There is little doubt that in some people there is a great deal more mental activity than in others. Is it possible that many people only use a small part of the brain they have?

I

Actions and How They Are Performed

ᚵᛁᛖ

We have been discussing how the brain deals with the messages it receives from the senses, and how it reduces them to a useful form by finding significant patterns in them. We have now to go a step further and see how these patterns or pictures are translated into actions, which enable the animal to satisfy its needs and to continue to live—actions which are often extremely complicated.

There seem to be two chief ways by which these actions are stimulated and controlled—and both ways have been developed in animals to a quite extraordinary degree.

INSTINCT

First, there is the *instinctive* response. The animal is in a situation which it has not met before, but nevertheless it is able to perform very complex actions, the purpose of which cannot be known to it. Under these circumstances the ability to perform these actions must be innate, i.e. the animal is born with it.

Chickens can run about soon after being hatched and will peck at any small, bright object; a calf or newly-born rabbit is soon able to suck from its mother. Birds can fly, when their wing feathers have developed, with little or no practice. These are all *complicated* muscular actions. They involve bringing great numbers of muscles into action, each in the right order and at the right time. The signals which stimulate these muscles must reach their destination at just the right times. These signals must be dispatched by the brain and it follows that in such cases the pattern of nervous stimulation which produces the action must be present in the animal's brain at birth only requires a suitable stimulus to cause it to function. Thus no doubt it is the feel of the mother's breast, or any similar object, which initiates the sucking. Similarly, young birds will gape, i.e. open their mouths for food. whenever a small object approaches the nest. The red-backed shrike has an innate tendency to impale its food on sharp thorns.

In all these cases the patterns of action are all present in the brain —imprinted, as it were, among the nerve connections and only requiring the appropriate stimulus to bring them into action.

This method has reached its greatest development among the insects, which carry out extraordinarily complex actions in their life cycles, obviously without any 'understanding' of their object. Fabre and other students of insect life have recorded many remarkable examples. For example, the hunting wasp, *Ammophila*, lays its eggs on the top of a caterpillar, which is alive and has merely been paralysed by injecting a nerve poison into the nerve centre of each of its segments. It is then placed in a hole in the ground which was previously prepared, which is then sealed and the caterpillar remains alive but immobile, ready to feed the larva when it hatches out.

Another wasp, *Eumenes*, constructs a clay urn, the lower part of which is filled with live caterpillars. Suspended from the top by a thread and out of reach of the caterpillars, is a single egg. When the egg hatches out the larva hangs on the thread and is able to eat the nearest caterpillars without danger. When it gets bigger it can descend from its thread and consume the rest.

The insect performs a quite extraordinary series of actions without any knowledge of what it is doing. It has been found that each series of this kind is a sequence. One step forward cannot be taken until the previous one is completed. Every step, when complete, provides the stimulus for the next. The series of actions can, as a rule, be only carried out in one order.

Students of instinct, such as Tinbergen, Lorenz and Bierens de Haan, have recognized that, to initiate an instinctive action, a particular sensory stimulus is required, which 'releases' the series of actions which follow. What it really does must be to 'release' a sequence of signals which pass along the nerves to the muscles and so cause the necessary muscular movements. The ability to make these nerve signals is obviously imprinted on the nervous system, waiting only for the proper sense stimulus to bring it into action.

Tinbergen has shown that the releaser is easily imitated and that it has to have certain features while others are unimportant.

There is some doubt as to how much latitude is possible in performing the actions. In many cases an insect is quite at a loss if the sequence of actions is interfered with. For example, if the clay cage of the *Eumenes* is broken, the wasp may mend it, but it will not place the egg inside. Its power of modifying the action to suit the circumstances is very limited; but cases in which the action can be varied have been noted.

LEARNING TO ACT

Although instinct is very remarkable, it obviously has great disadvantages as a basis of animal life. It does not, as a rule, offer the possibility of learning from previous experiences and therefore it is at a loss when presented with a new set of circumstances.

The 'intelligent' animals have developed a very different method of finding actions which are appropriate to the circumstances—the method of learning by trial and error. One feature of these actions is that they are first of all performed very badly. The movements of a young mammal are at first disorganized and it only gradually learns how to use its limbs effectively. It will try to repeat actions which produce satisfying results, and after many repetitions they become easy. This means that the nerve connections which enable them to be carried out are not initially present. They become established by being used, but when established the action can be repeated with very little trouble. Thus when a young kitten has 'learnt' to run, all the muscle actions occur in the correct sequence, without any attention being given to the details. Animals thus acquire a whole repertory of muscle sequences which they are able to perform—and accurately—in order to bring about desired actions.

To be useful these actions have to be controlled by the information which the sense impressions give the animal about his surroundings. We have seen that from this information he constructs a 'picture' of the surroundings—a picture which, as we have already seen, is not just a momentary photograph but an interpretation based on previous knowledge and experience. A way in which muscular actions were related to the 'picture' which an animal or person makes of his surroundings was suggested by Dr K. J. N. Craik, a Cambridge psychologist, who died in 1945. He suggested how human beings (and possibly animals) may make use of the 'model' or 'picture' of their surroundings in planning actions. The suggestion was that the brain keeps on trying out possible actions within the 'model' or 'picture' of the outside world, which it has constructed. It attempts to forecast the results of possible actions within the model and when one is found which appears to give a satisfactory result, the action may follow. For example, a man using a cricket ball must predict the result of his action. This prediction is made within the picture he has in his mind of his surroundings. Similarly, when a cat jumps on a mouse, the action is planned within the model or picture which the cat has made of his surroundings. As a result a whole complex matrix of muscular action, which is brought into play, is *planned* as a coherent whole.

This idea suggests also *how* the matrix of nervous signals which will be required to bring about the necessary muscular movements is assembled. 'Trying out' an action involves making all the nervous connections which will be required if the action is effected. Many of the connections will already exist because they belong to the group of connections which bring about a muscular movement which has been *learnt*. The animal only *selects* from those it has learnt a group of movements of which it can predict the result. It makes its selection within the model or picture of the circumstances surrounding it.

According to this, there is a very close relation between the organization of the sense impressions and the organization (or learning) of muscle movements. The two modes of organization have in fact been achieved together. The first task in the development of an infant is to make this link between his organization of sense impressions and his learning to perform muscle movements. In his first few months he gazes intently at bright objects and tries to touch them, feel them, suck them and so on. He is also trying to perform satisfying actions—such as reaching an object he sees, or sucking it and he is thus at the same time learning how to perform muscular movements.

It is probably very important that the construction of the picture of the world shall go on concurrently with the learning of muscular movements. The child in fact is learning to make muscular movements within his picture of the surroundings and the movements are helping him to construct his picture. The plan, as it emerges, is in fact a plan of possible actions. Our picture of the world is a strictly utilitarian one.

This method of dealing with experiences is obviously only possible in a long infancy, when the young animal is sheltered, fed and protected. The young animal is not 'teachable' initially—he learns for himself how to perform action by trial and error.

The advantages of such a method of organizing actions are very great. It permits of a great number of factors being taken into account in determining one action; it allows of a very close correspondence between the action and the circumstances, i.e. it permits of accurate prediction of the result of the action. It allows the animal to learn from his experiences. All this gives animals a degree of effectiveness which no simple system of conditioned reflexes could have. It also leaves possible a degree of freedom and spontaneity, because in the last resort they are able to and, in fact, must make a choice between the various possible actions which are open to them.

It must be recognized that there is always an element of spontaneity in an animal's response to its sensations, sometimes more prominent and sometimes less prominent. It occurs even in very simple organisms and is very deeply rooted in Nature. It existed, indeed, before the development of brains and nerves. The amoeba pushes out its pseudopodia in an apparently aimless way; its protoplasm moves first one way and then another without apparent rhyme or reason. The Paramecium oscillates endlessly in the water in its search for food. Such movements are perhaps a consequence or reflection of the Brownian movements of small particles as they are buffeted about by the ceaseless and chaotic thermal motions of matter.

It is a long way from this to even the most irregular movements of animals, but it seems a reasonable inference that undirected movements come first and are reduced to order. The animal does not so much have to *initiate* movements as to impose order and control on the aimless movements of its limbs. It has to co-ordinate many incoherent movements into purposeful and effective actions.

Craik's suggestion provides a possible way in which this is achieved. It is a method of finding solutions, by trial and error, of the problems set by the senses. The brain acts as a kind of supercomputer in solving these problems. Those movements which it foresess will probably be inadequate are rejected. The control narrows down the range of actions to those which seem to satisfy the requirements of the situation.

However, it is important to realize that an element of spontaneity remains, and is necessary because, otherwise, there would be no actions from which the most suitable could be selected. This spontaneity is perhaps a relic of the undirected movements of the young animal, of its playfulness when it is learning to co-ordinate its muscles with its sense impressions. A kitten uses its muscles in a frankly experimental way. The movements are at first spontaneous and undirected, and it learns only gradually to co-ordinate them so as to produce effective actions within its 'picture' of the surroundings. But even in the adult animal, there remains an element of play or adventure—call it what you will—which is necessary if the animal is to continue to live successfully. It may be very dangerous to lose this element of initiative, since an animal which can perform actions which are perfectly adapted to a particular environment may be unable to cope with changed conditions. The animals which have survived the changes caused by human activities are those which were adaptable enough to live and prosper under changed conditions. Thus the sparrow survives, but the fen buzzard is practically lost. Even now animals are discovered to be coping with new conditions, e.g. the tomtit has taken to breaking the metal foils which cover milk bottles; swallows have discovered the advantages of making use of the eaves of houses to build their nests. It would appear that even the most rigid instinctive actions must have involved initiative at one time. The instinctive action, like the laying of eggs in a living caterpillar, must originally have been a random impulse, which was successful and became imprinted on the inherited nervous pattern. We have to conclude that random impulses are often useful, but the balance between initiative and routine is a very delicate one. Too much initiative may be as destructive as too little. The animal is often poised on a razor-edge between the perils of deviating too much from a regular habit and too little.

FREE WILL

We can now ask whether animals, and human beings too, have any real power of making a choice between the various possible actions which they may be called upon to perform. In the last resort, do they have any *free will* in making a choice among the various possible actions—or, to put it another way, what is it which determines the choice which they do finally make? We have seen that the power of choosing varies very greatly. Some actions are almost automatic responses to the sensory stimulus; others are influenced to a greater or less degree by learning from similar experiences. In these cases the action is not a direct response to the sensation; it is obvious that it is modified by the memory records of earlier experiences, so that the action is the result not only of the present sensations, but also of what has happened in the past. The present sensations are therefore modified by taking their place and being interpreted in terms of the whole picture which the animal makes of his world. The action is determined to some extent by the whole previous life of the animal, and by what he has learnt about the world. Under these circumstances can we say that the animal really makes, or is capable of making a choice? Is not its action really predetermined—even if it is modified by the experiences of the past? Is it not still an inevitable consequence of all the influences, past or present, which are acting on it?

The answer to this seems to be that if an action is determined not only by the immediate sensations—by what an animal sees, hears and feels—but also by its past experience and what it has learnt throughout its life, there may be an element of uncertainty. If the action is brought about by a process involving past experiences, which are combined in various ways by trial and error or by the accident that sometimes one recollection and sometimes another may be predominant, we may expect that the action which emerges from a given situation may not be always the same, i.e. will not be completely predetermined.

We can therefore allow an animal some ability to 'choose' in its actions. The extent of its power of choosing will depend on its ability to distinguish between the various possibilities and the range of its knowledge. If its experience and learning are very limited, the power of choice will obviously be limited too. If its experience is extensive and it has learnt a great deal about the world and about the consequences of its actions, the effectiveness of its choice may be considerable.

In such a case, the action is determined not only by the present circumstances, and also by old experiences acting in a delayed way, but also by *what has happened* to these experiences in the animal's brain, i.e. what it has learnt from them, how far it has succeeded in combining them and extracting meaning from them—in putting two and two together. In other words, the action is determined to some extent by the personality of the animal, i.e. the way in which it differs from other animals, either in its original set up or in its history.

So we see that we cannot give a very simple answer to the question of whether an animal has freedom of choice between possible actions. From one point of view it might be considered that it has not, because, even if actions are determined by very complex influences, arising from the present and past, it is still determined by the sum total of all the effects present in the animal's brain.

Yet this is not a very useful way of describing the animal's action. It is more useful to regard the animal's brain as essentially an organ for co-ordinating all its actions; of bringing its whole life and experience to bear on each distinct action. The life of the animal under these conditions is not made up of isolated acts; it is a continuous activity in which past and present are always blended. The degree to which this is achieved of course varies enormously; but in the higher animals where actions are controlled very largely by learning, we are certainly justified in regarding this complex amalgam of past experiences and learnt abilities as providing 'personality', i.e. each animal is unique and therefore its responses contain at least a degree of idiosyncrasy. We can conclude that we are justified in allowing a degree of freedom of choice to the extent that the animal is capable of distinguishing the different possibilities.

XVII

Using Tools and Symbols

जूरे

Everything which has been said so far applies, at least to some extent, to the higher animals as well as to man. They have memory and recognize things; their acts are determined partly by their immediate sense impressions and partly by what they remember. They are capable of learning how to perform complicated actions; they appear to choose between possible actions and to base their choice to some extent on an estimate of the results which are likely to follow. We must ask, what is it in addition to all this which distinguishes a human being from an animal? Have we left out anything in our description which would be distinctive of human life?

There can be no doubt that two of the essential characteristics of human life are the extensive use of tools and of language. Both of these occur only to a very rudimentary extent in animals—although we could not say that they do not occur at all. For this reason we might perhaps be justified in thinking that human abilities are developments from abilities already existing in the animals. Let us consider then what such developments involve.

The changes necessary to transform apes into men have been listed by Dr R. K. J. Hayes[1] as follows:

(1) the hands are remodelled and reformed so as to enable them to use tools and weapons;

(2) the pelvis is developed to form a bone ring, which can carry the trunk upright;

(3) the vocal organs are refined so as to make them capable of producing articulated sounds of varying pitch;

(4) the brain undergoes an all-round development, with an improvement in memory and foresight and becomes capable of abstraction and symbolism;

[1] R. K. J. Hayes in *A.A.A.S.* 1954.

(5) new inborn tendencies are acquired to indulge in types of play which give the opportunity of developing muscular skills and a close correlation between muscular action and sense impressions.

This is a rather formidable list of 'improvements'. Their chief effect is to permit the accurate use of tools and the development of language.

Tools are external objects which are used as extensions of the limbs so as to increase their reach and performance. They are controlled by the brain in exactly the same manner as the limbs themselves. When a violinist plays, the muscles which operate the instrument are controlled by means of the information reaching the brain from the sense of touch and hearing. The nervous circle goes from the muscles to the instrument and re-enters the brain through the senses. The accurate use of tools thus depends on using the sense data to control precisely the muscular actions which are producing the movements of the tool. This is obviously not a new faculty, but only a more precise use of abilities similar to those which higher animals possess.

In a sense the human voice can also be regarded as a tool, which is controlled in exactly similar ways, i.e. I listen to the sound of my voice and modify it according to what I hear. The muscles which produce the voice are thus controlled through the sense of hearing.

It must have been discovered by early man that he could make sounds which influenced actions and so bring about desired results. Sounds could be produced which were either ingratiating or frightening or merely served as a signal to draw attention to something.

The voice thus took its place, like the limbs, as a means of bringing about actions. Just as human beings planned their muscular actions within their pictures of the world, so they also produced sounds as part of their reaction to the picture provided by the senses. In such sounds we see the origin of language. Certain sounds became associated with particular situations and thus acquired a meaning and thus, in time, a 'language' of sounds was built up. From this point of view the important thing about the language is that initially it is a muscular act—a series of useful and effective muscular responses to a given situation.

From this point of view it can be seen that the organization of language is perhaps a development of an ability which was already present in the animal brain, which already provided a means of organizing from the sense picture something of a very different nature, *viz.* appropriate muscular actions. It is not a very big step from this to the setting up of a mechanism for producing appropriate sounds and associating these sounds with situations. The sounds are very different in nature from the circumstances elucidating them. The word *tree* does not in any way resemble a tree; nor does the muscular effort required to produce this sound have any obvious connection. The significant thing is that the association of the word with the object is effected with great ease.

Language thus began as an association of sounds and of related muscular acts with certain elements of the sense picture. The human brain, as it has developed, provides an enormous extension of this type of connection.

The consequences have been remarkable and have led to the development of a kind of living which is quite different to anything found in the rest of the animal kingdom.

In the first place the association of different sounds with different kinds of objects leads to descriptive language. The sense impressions are replaced by something quite different, i.e. words. The words then offer an alternative representation of the world—a representation which is clearly not the same as the original sense picture, but one which can take its place. The prime characteristic of the human brain is the great ease and precision with which this transition from direct sense impressions to words, used as symbols, can take place.

Let us think, very briefly, of the consequences of the translation of the actual world into a substitute world of words. In the first place it provides the possibility of communication between one human being and another—which is only possible to a very limited extent in animals.

When I see a tree, the mental picture I have belongs to me alone. I cannot communicate what I see to any other person directly, but only by using symbols like *tree, green, tall, elm,* which call up similar impressions from his own experience. In this way, the actual world is replaced by a world of symbols, i.e. words which take the place of the actual world. This has had the most profound consequences for human life. It helps the discovery of the nature of the actual world, since words are themselves an analysis of the world, and putting together words is to perform operations, not in the actual world, but in the substitute mental world of symbols. The exploration of the actual world has been enormously assisted by making use of the symbolic substitute world—and in fact it would be impossible to get very far in any other way.

Secondly, words are clearly useless unless they are heard and understood by somebody, so that the new world of words is not a private world, but is essentially *shared* with other people. In this way human knowledge came into existence as something in which individuals can share, but which they cannot possess exclusively by themselves.

Human knowledge is thus quite different from the instinctive knowledge, if we could call it knowledge, of insects or from that of animals, who clearly acquire a 'practical' working knowledge of the world they live in, which is at least sufficient for them to live. Human beings have this 'practical' knowledge; but over and above it is the knowledge derived from the alternative world of symbols. As a rule the human being does not discover these symbols for himself—he learns them from others and he learns for himself the correspondences between the symbol and his own observations. It is often very difficult to distinguish direct interpretations of experience and those which are derived from the shared symbols.

In this way human life has become necessarily and essentially a communal life. The human being is like a radio station—being both a transmitter and a receiver. It is tuned in, as it were, to all or many of the other stations and is continually receiving and emitting messages. In fact the interpretations a person makes of his sense experiences are very much influenced by his symbolic picture, i.e. by the shared knowledge he has learnt from other people.

So we see that human beings, through their great ability to replace the actual world by a symbolic world, which goes alongside the real world and interacts with it all the time, have found a quite new way of living. The world of symbols is obviously not static. It is interacting with the real world all the time. Every new experience has to be fitted into the symbol world; and in the same way every act is determined, not only by the actual world, but by all sorts of considerations which come from the world of symbols.

The two worlds, the world of direct sense impressions and the world of symbols, go on side by side and the one helps to interpret the other. From the world of words and other symbols—the accumulated knowledge which we have acquired—we are helped to interpret what we see. What we do is obviously determined by the symbolic outlook to a considerable extent.

It is a characteristic of human life that it is not static—like the life of the bee or the life of animals, which necessarily go on in much the same way for many generations. For one thing, human knowledge is not stationary—the symbols which human beings use to interpret life to themselves develop or at least change from time to time. This is because human beings, although they can learn the meaning of symbols, have to interpret their own experiences for themselves. They must always be engaged in interpreting their sense impressions and in finding symbolic interpretations which are satisfactory to themselves and can be communicated to others. They naturally use accepted symbols a good deal, but because the act of interpretation is a personal one, the interpretations rarely remain unchanged for long and successive generations may find new ways of looking at things, which will lead to new ways of doing things. In other words the search for meanings in which human beings are engaged, leads to invention and discovery.

As a result of this the human way of living is dynamic. As I have already pointed out, it would be wrong to regard the animal way of life as completely static; but the human way has a totally different tempo of change.

To sum up, the peculiar ability of the mass of cells which make up the human brain is not only to make a picture or model of the world from the information it obtains from the senses but to construct an alternative substitute world of symbols, which is a shared superstructure of human life. Everything human depends on this ability of human beings to live at one and the same time on these two levels—the level of direct experience and the level of symbols. The direct experience belongs to the individual alone; the symbolic level is necessarily shared because the symbols of which it is made and the ways in which they are combined are a communal possession.

Is the Brain a Calculating Machine?

I have discussed at some length the various abilities of the remarkable mass of cells which forms the human brain because it has frequently been claimed in recent years that suitable models for brain action are to be found in machines which really parallel only a very small part of the whole performance. There is no doubt that many of the simpler types of response of brains can be copied by machines. The latter can be provided with *sense organs,* which detect and respond to sounds and light and even to other physical agencies, such as radio waves, for which we have no sense organ; they can also be provided with a *memory,* since data can be put into the machine (often in the form of punched cards) and stored away for future use; with the power of *recognition,* in that the data supplied can be compared with previously established standards (e.g. a slot machine, which can recognize the proper coins and reject others; and finally with the power of *prediction,* as when a gun predictor follows an aeroplane and causes a gun to deliver a shell, not where the aeroplane was, but where it will be when the shell arrives. Machines can also be provided with controllers (feed-back) which maintain constant conditions, e.g. of temperature or pressure or speed, and in this way resemble the organism which maintains itself in the narrow range of conditions in which it can function.

This is an impressive list and could no doubt be extended. It might suggest that the analogy between brains and machines is a very close one. Attempts to develop these analogies have been encouraged very much by the fact that the mode of operation of modern electronic computors is not unlike what goes on in the brain, which, as we have seen, consists of an enormous number of neurones, connected together into a very complex network by thread-like connections (Fig. 26). The nerve fibres entering the grey matter of the brain are connected with the cells by small swellings or knobs which are called synapses. This junction has the special property that it will not let signals pass until they reach a certain strength. The synapse thus gives an 'all or none' response; if the signal is strong enough it passes; below a certain strength nothing happens.

One nerve may be joined in this way with many nerve cells, and each nerve cell has synaptic contacts with many different nerves. This provides an enormous number of pathways between the nerve cells.

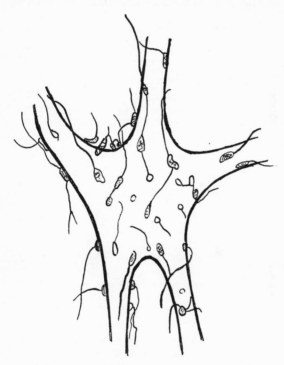

FIG. 26. A mammalian motor neurone, showing various sizes of synoptic knobs, several of which are often attached to one nerve fibre. (Adapted from J. C. Eccles, *The Neurophysiological Basis of Mind*. [Oxford Press])

In order to excite a nerve cell, a definite number of signals must reach it within a definite period through these synapses. When it is excited, it fires a 'volley', i.e. a complete signal, through the axon going from it. This 'volley' is independent of the nature of the stimulus, provided that it is sufficient. The axon usually branches before it reaches other nerve cells, so that the excitation may reach numerous other cells.

In the cerebral cortex it is difficult to recognize definite points of contact between the nerve cells. The latter often have fine thread-like appendages called dendrites and the axons from other nerve cells often split into many branches (Fig. 27). It is often seen that the branches of the coming-in axon runs parallel with the branching arms of the dendrites for a distance and stimulation passes from one fibre to the other in this region and thus into a new nerve cell.

When a neurone has fired a 'volley' there is a refractory period,

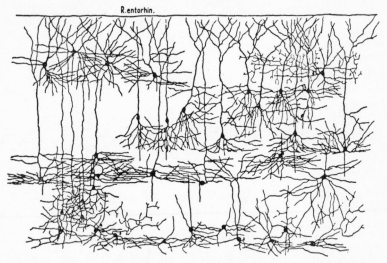

FIG. 27. Typical neurones and their branching connections, found in different layers of the cerebral cortex of an ape. (From Dr Lorenté de No's article in Fulton's *Physiology of the Nervous System*. [Oxford University Press])

which lasts for about a thousandth of a second, during which it cannot be stimulated again. The neurone can also be inhibited, i.e. a signal from another neurone will bring it into a state in which it cannot fire.

The neurone thus resembles a relay which repeats a sufficiently strong signal and which remains 'dead' for the 'refractory period' after being fired. To a considerable extent this kind of behaviour can be reproduced by arrangements of thermionic valves. They act as relays and can be arranged so that they will respond only to signals above a certain strength. They also have a recovery period after 'firing' and can be prevented from firing at all.

A great deal of effort has been devoted to attempts to build up models, using these principles, which will possess at least some of the abilities of brains. In the first place, can we find a basis for memory? A good many years ago Dr Lorenté de No pointed out that a number of neurones arranged in a circle would act as a permanently reverberating circuit. A pattern of impulses fed into the circuit at any point will continue to circulate indefinitely. It is only necessary that the neurones should be able to provide sufficient energy and that the ring should be sufficiently long so that the first neurone is in a receptive state when the message arrives back. Patterns of impulses could thus be stored in the brain in a permanent or semi-permanent form. Drs McCulloch and Pitts have investigated mathematically the properties of such networks of neurones and suggested that they provide a possible basis of memory since the patterns of impulses will continue to circulate long after the immediate occasion which produced them has passed.

Although there is no doubt that innumerable circuits exist in the brain, it is doubtful if this suggestion offers a satisfactory theory of memory. Lashley has extended the idea somewhat. If the brain contains innumerable circuits, how does a circulating impulse know how to ⟨. . .⟩ its own circuit and to ignore many others? Lashley has suggested ⟨. . .⟩ pattern of excitation spreads out from the neurones ⟨. . .⟩mulated. The activity which starts at one point in the cortex may spread out and give rise to radiating waves of activity. When many points are stimulated simultaneously, the different waves of activity will interact with each other like the waves formed when a number of stones are thrown into a pond, giving rise to interference patterns and to a pattern of standing waves. This would perhaps give a basis for understanding how general characteristics (called 'universals') are recognized, irrespective of their size and position. The interference patterns finally produced would be similar, and would not depend on such details.

An alternative proposal was made by Drs McCulloch and Pitts. They suggested that the sensory impulses are received on several layers of neurones, which are, as it were, tuned to different scales of magnitude. Each of these is brought, in turn, into a receptive condition by a 'scanning' mechanism. The signals sent on to the reverberating circuits are thus the sum or average of those produced by the original pattern, when measured on the different scales, so that what matters is the essential character of the pattern rather than its size or position.

Hebb has gone still further and suggested that the conducting circuits between neurones are themselves modified by the passage of

K

impulses, so that the patterns which are frequently excited tend to become permanent. Hebb thinks that the change is to be regarded as a kind of growth process, as a result of which the terminations of the axons increase in size as the result of the passage of impulses. This means that although a short-lived memory might be maintained by a reverberating circuit of neurones, if stimulation is frequently repeated, it will become very much easier to produce the stimulated pattern. The memory will then be, as it were, 'built in' to the cortical structure and will not be destroyed by electric shocks and other disturbances.

These proposals are obviously very sketchy and incomplete and readers will have no difficulty in concluding that no really adequate models of brain action exist—except for perhaps the very simplest types of action.

The existence of memory obviously requires that patterns of some sort based on the original sense stimuli are stored somewhere in the brain. The form in which this storage is effected is not really known. It is not necessary to suppose that the original impulses go on circulating in the brain for ever. What is required is a mechanism which will store them up in such a form that they can be repeated. Th... could occur, as Hebb suggested, by structural change[...] nections between the neurones, as a result of which a [...] tern of stimulation is easily re-established. Another pos[...] the impulses are stored in the neurones themselves, e.g. when a s[...] of impulses reaches a neurone, it may bring about permanent changes in its structure of such a kind that the neurone will be capable of emitting the same series of impulses at a future time. Thus the neurone may not only be a receptor of signals and a relay; but a repeater unit. It will store up patterns of impulses and repeat them at a later stage. However such a process has not been demonstrated.

As I have explained, the memory mechanism is quite fundamental to brain action. Without memory there can be no recognition and no learning. But it is also probable that the memory is not a simple memory of the actual original sensations but of the interpretation which is made of them. It is the *meanings* which are remembered, rather than the sensations themselves. The situation is therefore a very complex one and it is difficult to separate one aspect from another. But the very least we can say is that behind the neurones in which the immediate sense impressions are received, there must be others in which they are compared and interpreted in terms of the memory record of previous experiences. That is, the immediate sensations find their places in the continuing record of the structure of experience which has been gradually built up during all our lives.

It is this feature which gives continuity to our lives and to that of all animals with a developed brain. We must therefore picture the brain, not merely as a kind of telephone exchange for linking senses with muscles, but as something which stores up to some extent everything which has been experienced and unites it with the present. It is essentially an organ of continuity and the very least that we can say about its mechanism is that it must provide a means by which the present can take its place *within* the record of the past. A calculating machine which resembled a brain would thus have to be permanently modified by every operation it performed. When presented with a sequence of numbers, it would have to recognize in them features like previous sequences, and perform operations which had produced successful results before. It would be rather boring to press this any further; but I think it will be evident that the gap between the brain and the machine is very great. Indeed the real work of the machine is still being done by the operators who set it up.

We must however enquire a little further about what goes on in real brains. We have found that patterns of stimulation arrive from the senses in the receptor areas, and from these patterns of excitation spread out through innumerable circuits to other regions. In these regions they meet and are compared with patterns arising from previous experiences. How this is done we hardly know, as we do not know how the memory record is stored, and how it is made available for comparison. But it is evident that the original sensations are dealt with at more than one level and finally we come to the level of awareness and consciousness, at which the interpretation which has been made is finally judged and action is set in motion or, possibly, no action is decided upon.

What is this level of consciousness? It seems as if there is something in the brain which is capable of 'looking at' the images as they are formed at lower levels, which may either come from the actual sensory impressions or from the memory record. We might, as an analogy, think of the lower levels as like a television set which receives impulses and produces a picture from them. To produce a picture is, however, not to be conscious of it; and here we come to perhaps the greatest mystery and the most difficult feature in the whole range of living phenomena.

For a scientist, consciousness and awareness are subjective phenomena which are not capable of instrumental verification. We are aware of what we experience ourselves, e.g. the sensation of green when looking at a green field. We have absolutely no way of telling what sensations other people are aware of, except from what they tell us about their experiences. The sensation of green, which I am aware of, is thus a subjective phenomena which cannot be measured by scientific instruments in the same way as a nerve impulse. For this reason many scientists think that the subjective aspect of sensations should not be considered in attempting a scientific account of the brain.

I think, however, that such subjective feelings and 'sensations' are a legitimate study of science. While it is true that we are only directly aware of our own sensations, yet we do not doubt that other people have similar ones, as their behaviour only makes sense if we assume, for example, that they see and hear and feel substantially what we see and hear and feel ourselves. So it will be necessary to bring sensations into the scientific picture somehow, although at present we have practically no idea as to how it can be done. There is very little doubt that the 'sensation' is connected with what goes on in the nerve fibres because, as Dr Penfield has shown, the electrical stimulation of exposed parts of the brain causes sensations, e.g. coloured lights and feelings, like a tingling in the extremities and so on. In fact it is to some extent possible to locate the cells which are concerned with vision or feeling by experiments of this kind; but the fact that stimulating a particular group of cells with electric currents produces a sensation of green does not prove that the sensation actually arises there. It may well be that the pattern of excitation which is started in these cells spreads to other parts of the brain.

In recent years some remarkable discoveries about this memory record have also been made by Dr Penfield. In the course of operations on the exposed brain, which are performed on epileptic patients with the object of discovering and eradicating the region in which the epileptic seizure originates, the cortex is stimulated electrically by means of electrodes placed at different points. The operation is performed without anaesthesia and the patient is able to describe his experiences. In some cases the effect of stimulation was to cause memories of long-forgotten events to return into the consciousness. For example, Dr Penfield states[1] that M.M. heard 'a mother calling her little boy' when point 11 on the first temporal convolution was stimulated. When it was repeated at once, she heard the same thing. When repeated twice at the same point, she heard it each time, and she recognized she was near her childhood home.

At point 12 nearby, on the same convolution, stimulation caused her to hear a man's voice and a woman's voice 'down the river somewhere' and she saw the river. It was at a place 'I was visiting', she said, 'when I was a child'.

Three minutes later, while the electrode was held in place 13, she

[1] *Proc. Nat. Acad. Sciences* (U.S.), **44**, 59 (1958).

exclaimed that she heard voices late at night and that she saw the 'big wagons they used to haul the animals (of a circus) in'.

Eleven minutes later, the original point 11 was stimulated again. She no longer heard the mother calling her little boy. Instead she heard 'the voices of people calling from building to building'.

Later still, when a coated electrode was inserted at 17 so as to stimulate the first temporal convolution deep down in the fissure of Sylvius, she said, 'I had . . . a familiar memory, in an office somewhere. I could see the desks. I was there, and someone was calling to me, a man leaning on a desk with a pencil in his hand'.

Dr Penfield concludes that there is in the brain a permanent record of the stream of consciousness, which is preserved in amazing detail. The detail cannot be recalled to the memory by voluntary effort. All that can be recalled as a rule are rather vague generalizations and summaries of the previous experiences. Yet these are sufficient for recognition, for example, of persons or scenes one has seen before.

XIX

Ageing and Death

꘭

We have followed as far as we can the extraordinary developments of the life of cells. We must now turn to another question and ask why, if their organization is so perfect and well adapted to their functions, should they not continue to live, failing accidents, at least as long as they are provided with the necessary nutriments and with a suitable environment?

One could perhaps draw a distinction between unicellular organisms and multicellular organisms. It has often been suggested that the former are effectively immortal, since they undergo repeated subdivision and, given enough food material, they need never die. However, the distinction between unicellular and multicellular organisms in this respect is probably more apparent than real. A colony of cells will go on increasing its numbers by cell division until it has used up the food materials in its particular environment. No colony has the whole world to expand into, if for no other reason than that, sooner or later, it will come into competition with other organisms. When the available food has been used up, the majority of the cells must die, and new cells can be formed only so far as fresh food becomes available. It often happens also that a colony of cells destroys its environment by producing waste products, e.g. acids, in which it cannot grow. Many unicellular organisms developed ways of escaping from this situation, e.g. by producing spores, which may be able to establish a new colony elsewhere. But in this case the colony is in a similar situation as that of multicellular organisms, which die after forming new individuals from special cells like the sperm and egg. The colony of single cells behaves very similarly when it has exhausted its habitat. It dies, but a few cells or spores may escape and found a new colony elsewhere.

However, this analogy is rather superficial. The multicellular animal is usually mobile and can get away from its waste products. It does not have to die because it has either used up the nutriments around it, or because it has fouled its environment. Are we to suppose that it dies because it has fouled its 'internal environment', i.e. that waste products gradually accumulate inside the organism, which clog the efficient working of the different organs and in the end cause death?

It is certain that in many organisms ageing processes do occur. Even with animals kept in good surroundings with adequate food and protected from other predatory organisms the organism as a whole gets less efficient. The bodily processes slow down, the muscles become less effective, the bones often become brittle, many tissues undergo degenerative changes—e.g. tendons become less elastic, and growth processes, e.g. growth of hair and healing of wounds, slow down, with the result that the repair of damages caused by wear and tear becomes less effective. Finally, some vital organ ceases to function and the organism as a whole ceases to live.

It has been very difficult to discover why organisms age in this way and what determines the average length of life. In the natural state ageing processes are rarely encountered because death usually occurs owing to some mischance while the animal is still in its prime. Yet there is no doubt that animals which are carefully maintained, live for various characteristic average periods. It has been suggested, as I mentioned above, that organs become clogged by waste products, or by substances of a poisonous nature which they are unable to get rid of. This may be so, although it has not been clearly demonstrated. In a more general sense it can be supposed that cells will only function efficiently for a limited period. Membranes may break down or become clogged and synthetic mechanisms may begin to work incorrectly. Accidental damage may occur in the cell which it is unable to repair.

On the other hand, it seems to be true that tissues which are capable of regenerating themselves by cell division will continue to function, possibly indefinitely. Cell cultures continue to grow (by cell division) in artificial media for many generations, long after the animal from which the cells were obtained has died. Sea urchins live indefinitely, because all their cells undergo continuous replacement.

This would seem to indicate that the cell has a limited life time and will die unless it is able to regenerate itself by cell division. This does not explain why animals have such very different life spans. Different mammals are extraordinarily similar in their general construction. They have very similar organs which function in similar ways and produce similar substances and apparently are constructed of similar kinds of cells. The pancreas of different mammals produce insulins and enzymes which are almost interchangeable. Yet, nothwithstanding their close similarity, the life times of such cells within the different mammals vary enormously. This suggests that the determining factor is not a characteristic of the individual cells, but something which is determined by the organism as a whole.

We are still ignorant of what this factor is which determines the life span of animals. There are some suggestive facts. Frequently the life span is proportional to the size of the animal. This may be connected with the fact that the life span is proportional to the time taken by the animal to reach maturity, i.e. to reach its full size with all its organs functioning. It has even been shown that if the attainment of maturity is artificially delayed, e.g. by keeping the immature animal very short of food, the life span is thereby increased. Some fishes which apparently continue to grow indefinitely also live for very long periods. This suggests that ageing begins when growth ceases. But why should the ageing process take so much longer with a large animal like an elephant than with mice or rabbits? It would appear that the ageing process is slower with a larger number of cells than with a smaller collection. This may perhaps indicate that the cells of an organ help each other and in a large organ there is a greater possibility of the wear and tear, which must occur in some cells, being made up by others.

However, we must not suppose that increase of life span is necessarily desirable. If there were no death, then there could not be any new individuals either. Unless there were a continual stream of new individuals, there could not be any evolution. Other things being equal there will be a greater possibility of evolutionary changes if the time from one generation to the next is as short as possible. The minimum time is that required for the individual to come to maturity and to produce and launch the next generation. From an evolutionary point of view, any longer life-time is wasteful; but of course in order that each generation shall be able to perform its duties, there has to be some margin of viability and under favourable conditions, animals will usually be able to live for a time after their useful reproductive life has finished. From this, it would seem that the life span is determined biologically by the time taken for the animal to reach full maturity and produce offspring. The larger and more complex the organism, the greater is the time required for this development. Beyond this it may well be that there is an evolutionary advantage in individuals not living too long and that this has led to the development of factors in the organisms which result in ageing processes occurring at the end of the reproductive period.

If this is correct, it would seem that the life span is determined by the interplay of two effects—the necessity of living long enough to start off the new generation and, having performed this task, the fact that a further life time is unnecessary and, in many respects, harmful to the well-being and development of the species. It is quite possible that mechanisms exist in organisms which bring about this limitation of the life period, when the biologically useful period is over, but we do not know what these mechanisms are.

We can conclude that most organisms have not only a mechanism for reproduction and growth, but also an ageing mechanism which automatically brings life to a gradual end when the useful period is over. We must regard this ageing mechanism as 'built in' to the cells as an essential feature of their construction, a kind of biological clock with a time scale which is characteristic of each species. We do not know where the clock is located. It has often been thought that ageing is brought about by the failure of one or other of the endocrine glands and attempts have been made to produce rejuvenation by grafting glands or injecting glandular extracts, e.g. from the testicles of juvenile animals. These treatments have not had more than a very limited success. Although they are capable of supplementing to some extent the operation of failing glands, they do not prevent the ageing process as a whole.

It might be said that these considerations do not apply to mankind, which is no longer subject to evolutionary change. While it is true that over the historic period no definite evolutionary trends seem to have been noted, we cannot be certain that evolution is not actually taking place or that selection of certain types is not actively occurring. However, in human communities, factors other than simple reproduction and survival assume a much greater importance than in animal communities. It can be argued that survival of the community depends on qualities such as 'wisdom', i.e. the correct interpretation of experience, in which age is a definite advantage. It can be argued and was argued for example by Bernard Shaw that human beings usually die or become senile at an age when their experience would be of great value to the community and also before they have made use of their full potentiality. However, Shaw's picture of life among the ancients is not a very attractive one and not many people would regard it as particularly desirable to live to 150 just to sit and contemplate.

Life in an aged population would really be very static, unless human nature changed a good deal. Even now most of the initiative and new ideas come from the comparatively young. It would seem to be better to have a continuous stream of new and vigorous persons than to extend the individual life period considerably. If the average life span were, say, 120 or 150 years, the whole tempo of life would be different. Education would continue up to the age of 30 or 40; full maturity from 40 to 100 or 120 and a gradual decline into old age from the age of 100 upwards. It is not at all certain that this would produce any improvement on the present conditions. It would greatly reduce the tempo of change in human life. There would not be the same urge to get things done. Young men would have to wait very much longer for their chances. Many of the eminent people who died during the last fifty years would still be alive and probably, if their health were reasonably good, occupying the same posts which they held in about 1910 to 1920. The result would be that in the end the longer life span would produce exactly the same problems and difficulties as the present one. Indeed it seems likely that the present span of life is reasonable in relation to and perhaps determined by the speed of human life processes. The normal span is already long enough for individuals to develop their potentialities to a reasonable extent and to give a sufficient balance between initiative and experience, which is required if human society is to be neither stagnant nor juvenile. Of course, it is likely that under existing conditions a great many people do not succeed in developing their full possibilities, but this is a fault of the organization of society, which does not offer sufficient opportunities for development, rather than of the time available. The people who have not developed a satisfying life or have not found out how to use their full abilities during their first sixty years are unlikely to do much better with another thirty or forty.

One other possibility may be mentioned—that one factor which limits the possible development of human beings and therefore their valuable life, is the *quantity* of brain available. There may be a limit to the number of new impressions which a brain can effectively utilize. It seems to be a general experience that the ability to entertain new ideas and absorb new experiences diminishes with advancing age. New experiences have to be assimilated into the accumulated patterns of experience that have been developing throughout life. Older people often find it difficult to adapt their thinking to new conditions and to the new ideas of a new generation. This is because their thinking is organized around conceptions which are no longer valid— their brains in fact contain great organizations of experience which are no longer of any value, because the circumstances they were based on have passed away. The structure of their brains does not permit them to cast away all this now useless lumber and start again. The only way in fact in which they could start again is by being reborn and starting with the brain of a newborn infant and learning everything afresh in the new environment. This is exactly what occurs under the present conditions of human life.

XX

Life in the Universe

🙞🙜

We started with simple atoms and molecules—the building bricks of all the complex patterns which have been discovered in living things. We then worked our way upwards through proteins and enzymes to the larger aggregations, such as nucleoproteins, which occur in chromosomes and viruses and in the cytoplasm of cells. The living cell, taken as a whole, represents a much higher level of complication still, since many of these structures must be present in every living cell in a precisely organized manner. It is only at this stage that we reach a level which is recognizably living, in the sense that everything necessary for continuing life in a natural environment is present.

It is probable that the smallest visible cell contains about a quarter of a million protein molecules of many kinds and larger cells many more. Taking the average protein molecule as containing about 20,000 atoms, we see that the smallest independently living units contain something like five thousand million (5,000,000,000) atoms, united into molecules of great complexity and all the molecules organized into a single functioning whole.

There are as many or more cells in the human body than atoms in a single cell, so that the cell comes midway in the scale of complexity between atoms and man. If we were to take another step of the same order of magnitude, we should have to include a great deal of the visible universe! Man is therefore in a midway position between the minute atoms of which the universe is constructed and the almost unimaginable whole. It is clear from this that human beings and other large animals are of colossal dimensions on an atomic scale and hardly insignficant even when judged on a cosmic scale (see Fig. 28).

In a broad sense we have been tracing the great landmarks in the ascent of life. They are four in number, although no doubt many intermediate gradations could be recognized. The first stage, the complete elaboration of the basic chemistry of life, is already achieved in the simple free-living cells and, very broadly speaking, it undergoes no further change. The second stage, the organization of numerous cells into large organisms, involves further steps, in which there is an increase in complexity of the same order of magnitude as that in the elaboration of the cells from simple molecules. But the problems of

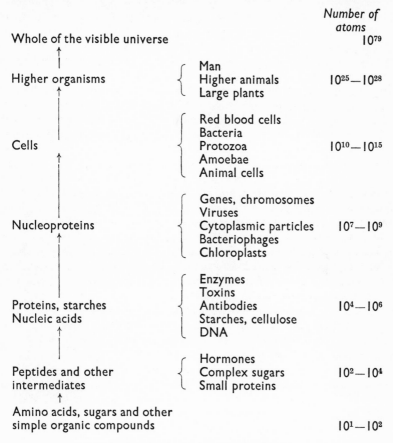

		Number of atoms
Whole of the visible universe		10^{79}
Higher organisms	Man Higher animals Large plants	10^{25}—10^{28}
Cells	Red blood cells Bacteria Protozoa Amoebae Animal cells	10^{10}—10^{15}
Nucleoproteins	Genes, chromosomes Viruses Cytoplasmic particles Bacteriophages Chloroplasts	10^{7}—10^{9}
Proteins, starches Nucleic acids	Enzymes Toxins Antibodies Starches, cellulose DNA	10^{4}—10^{6}
Peptides and other intermediates	Hormones Complex sugars Small proteins	10^{2}—10^{4}
Amino acids, sugars and other simple organic compounds		10^{1}—10^{2}

FIG. 28. Hierarchy of natural structures

organization are different. They involve the processes of differentiation, specialization and growth, which are involved in uniting vast numbers of cells into a single organism. These processes are very little understood.

The third stage occurred when the organism became a mobile animal and acquired muscles to move about, sense organs to tell it about its environment and a brain to join them together. The animal in this way became aware of the world it lived in, at least to a limited extent.

The fourth great stage in the ascent of life, which must be regarded as still in its infancy, is the attainment by man of the power to replace the actual world, as it is experienced, by a world of symbolic equivalents, which can be manipulated in the mind and rearranged. As I have pointed out, this permits the storing of experiences, so that it becomes possible to have knowledge which is not based on the limited experience of each individual. As a result of this, human knowledge exists and grows independently of the individuals who make some use of it. It possesses a dynamism of its own. The knowledge and the symbolisms in which it is expressed and the ways of thinking and acting to which these give rise, give human societies their peculiar character. The society becomes in fact a *superorganism*, because the individual cannot live to more than a very partial extent without it and the way he lives is largely determined, not by his own simple reactions to his experience, but by the knowledge and ways of living which the superorganism has arrived at.

There are of course other superorganisms besides the human ones, e.g. those created by the social insects, but so far as we know, the latter are held together by instinct. The human superorganisms are characterized by shared knowledge, which, as we have seen, is achieved by the human ability to turn experiences into symbolic equivalents which can be passed from person to person. The superstructure of communal knowledge provides a kind of scaffolding within which the life of every individual is lived. It is not a static scaffolding, but one which changes continuously. For this reason the life of an individual in Western Europe in the twentieth century for example, is quite different to that of a similar individual a hundred years earlier, although his mental capacities may be similar. Not only does his mind operate on different data, but it operates in different ways which are determined by the very different symbolic environment in which he lives. The individual life is an interaction between the floating climate of ideas and his own personal reaction to them.

The shared mass of ideas, which do not belong to any one person exclusively, but are the possession of a whole community, or a large part of it, form what may be regarded as a *collective mind*, which possesses a kind of life of its own. It develops according to its own laws or inner necessities. This has been clearly recognized in the many histories which have been written about the development of this or that aspect of human thought. For example, we can recognize clearly the lines of development of western music or science through many generations of different people.

In conclusion, readers may ask what human meaning can be extracted from the knowledge which has been gained of the cell, its construction and its achievements. Does it tell us anything about the meaning of life? In the first place, it should be explained that science does not concern itself with ultimate meanings; it is only concerned with what it finds out about things as they exist and the relations between them. It does ask how they came to be in their present state, but it does not ask what they exist for or what is the object of it all. Many scientists deny that there is any sense in such questions. Yet, although science does not provide answers, human beings persistently look for them and have always wanted to round off their useful knowledge by some conception of the meaning of it all. It is, in fact, a necessity of the human mind to have some sort of a unifying conception which will hold together all the fragments of knowledge which have been acquired and which is capable of giving meaning and perspective to human life as it progresses from one generation to another.[1] So from a human point of view, we are justified in asking whether we can find any meaning in the extraordinary pageant of events which has been disclosed. Is it all just an accident—as some scientists have suggested—the result of an extremely improbable event which brought together the atoms, forming the first self-reproducing system; so giving rise to the first germ of life? Or, as has been suggested here, is it not inevitable that such complex systems will be formed whenever suitable conditions occur, i.e. water, radiation and a variety of inorganic substances? Whichever may be the correct view of the origin of life, there can be no doubt that in living systems, as they have evolved and as we find them today, we have chemical systems of a very complicated kind, which form a single family of living things. Are we then justified in regarding life, in all its variety, as merely an exhibition of an immensely complicated chemistry?

I think we cannot avoid concluding that this is correct as far as it goes, but it is not the whole truth. We can say in this, as in other fields, that the whole is greater than the parts. We may be able to break down the organism into its cells, and the cells into the interlocking component cycles of activity, yet the functioning cell is more than the sum of the chemical processes of which it is made up and the organism is more than the sum of the cells of which it is composed. This can be illustrated by a simpler example. If we combine a

[1] I cannot justify this statement here, but readers who are interested will find a discussion in my book *Science and Human Life* (Pergamon Press).

number of atoms of carbon, hydrogen, nitrogen and oxygen together in a particular way, we obtain the vivid blue dye, methylene blue. We could not have suspected from what we knew of these atoms that, when combined in this way, they would exhibit this property. Nevertheless, once we have the dye, we may be able to account for its properties in terms of the atoms and their mode of combination. We can, for example, account for the colour as due to the oscillation of electrons in a particular cyclic molecular framework, and this can be 'explained' in terms of the electronic structure of the atoms themselves. If necessary we may and we frequently must add to our description of the atoms in order to enable us to account for methylene blue and other substances in terms of them, but we could hardly have predicted methylene blue (or other dyes) if we were completely ignorant of its existence and behaviour.

We can well believe that the ability to produce such dyes is implicit in the atoms of carbon, nitrogen, etc, but it lies dormant until such compounds are actually made. We can say that a new property, the vivid blue colour, *emerges* in a particular combination. While the possibility is implicit in the atoms, it is essentially a property of the *whole* of the combination and not of its separate parts.

In just the same way we see new kinds of behaviour emerging at the different levels of life, which could hardly have been predicted if only the simpler systems which are made use of were known.

The new level of organization can be analysed into its component mechanisms, and the new organization is implicit in the components, but nevertheless when it has been achieved, something new has appeared, which is more than the sum of the separate mechanisms of which it is made up.

From this point of view, we see, as Bergson did in his concept of emergent evolution, that in the course of evolution there has not only been an increase of complexity of the parts, but also the emergence of new properties, which although they are *potentially* present in the simpler systems, do not really exist until they are actually produced and when they are achieved are essentially more than the isolated parts.

Therefore, although we are entitled to see in life a mechanical process, a consequence of the natural combining possibilities of atoms when supplied with energy, leading to the formation of self-perpetuating compounds which can make use of solar energy and impose their pattern on the environment and thus give rise to ever more and more complex organizations, yet we must also see this as providing a basis for the emergence of new 'wholes' with types of behaviour which we should not have suspected, although they were nevertheless present potentially all the time.

Judging by the uniformity of Nature as we see it here, life must have appeared in many places in the Universe, wherever the necessary conditions—water, light and simple compounds—exist. We must think of living things, at various levels of complexity, as part and parcel of the Universe of light, heat and material atoms. We ought not to think of living organizations merely as complex mechanisms; they are more than this. They exist in their own right, as emergent creations of the 'élan vital' or 'life force', call it what you will. Mentality, whatever it is—we know very little at present—also cannot be regarded as an outsider, but as implicit from the start, waiting to be realized. We can see the Universe, comprising both matter and life, as one process; though in extent, duration and complexity it is beyond our comprehension. We must believe one thing about it, although we cannot prove it, but it is a reasonable conclusion from what we do know, that in some sense the end was implied in the beginning.

A few years ago it was fashionable to think of life as a remote and improbable accident in a life-less Universe. Life was thought of, as Jeans said,[1] as 'an unimportant by-product' in 'a Universe which was clearly not designed for life, and which, to all appearances, is either totally indifferent or definitely hostile to it'. It seemed, he said, 'incredible that the Universe can have been designed primarily to produce life like our own; had it been so, surely we might have expected to find a better proportion between the magnitude of the mechanism and the amount of the product'.

However, although the size of the mechanism is clearly fantastic, we do not know the amount of the 'product'. It could be argued just as easily that the colossal dimensions of the Universe ensure that the conditions (energy, stability, environment) required for the development of life will occur in many places. To argue that life is an improbable accident is no more cogent than to suggest that the Universe itself is improbable and unlikely. Perhaps it is, but it does exist and we can only accept it. In the same way it is only reasonable, although our knowledge is so limited, to accept life, and also mentality, as something which is normal and even inevitable.

It is just as likely that the Universe was designed primarily to produce life like our own, as the reverse. That men do exist, with all their extraordinary abilities and potentialities, is the primary fact of human life and it is better to put that and all that is implied by it in the forefront of our picture of the world, than to suggest that it is all an improbable accident.

[1] *The Mysterious Universe* (Cambridge University Press).

L

TABLE I. The Twenty Commonest Amino Acids of which Proteins are Constructed

General Formula $R.CH\!<^{NH_2}_{CO_2H}$

Name	Abbreviation	R	Name	Abbreviation	R
Glycine	gly		Proline	pro	$\left[\begin{array}{l} CH_2.CH_2 \\ \hphantom{CH_2.}{>}CH.CO_2 \\ CH_2.NH \end{array}\right]^{\dagger}$
Alanine	ala	CH_3	Aspartic Acid	asp	$HOOC.CH_2$
Valine	val	$(CH_3)_2.CH$	Asparigine	—	$H_2NOC.CH_2$
Leucine	leu	$(CH_3)_2.CH.CH_2$	Glutamic acid	glu	$HOOC.CH_2.CH_2$
iso-Leucine	ileu	$\begin{array}{l} C_2H_5 \\ \hphantom{C_2H}{>}CH \\ CH_3 \end{array}$	Glutamine	—	$H_2NOC.CH_2.CH_2$
Phenylalanine	phe	$C_6H_5.CH_2$	Arginine	arg	$H_2N.C(NH).NH.CH_2(CH_2)_2$
Tyrosine	tyr	$HO.C_6H_5.CH_2$	Lysine	lys	$H_2N.CH_2.CH_2.CH_2$
Serine	ser	$HO.CH_2$	Histidine	his	$\begin{array}{l} N.CH \\ \hphantom{N.}{\cdot}C.CH_2 \\ CH.NH. \end{array}$
Threonine	thr	$\begin{array}{l} CH_2\ CHOH \end{array}$	Cysteine*	cys	$HS.CH_2$
Tryptophane	try	$\begin{array}{l} CH_2 \\ \text{(indole ring) } NH \end{array}$	Methionine	met	$CH_3.S.CH_2.CH_2$

*Cystine: $NH_2\!>\!CH.CH_2.S.S.CH_2.CH\!<^{NH_2}_{CO_2H}$ $^{}_{CO_2H}$ is formed from two cysteine molecules joined together

†This is the whole formula

CH₃ — Riboflavin

$CH_2OHC \cdot CHOH \cdot C \cdot NH \cdot CH_2CH_2COOH$

Pantothenic acid

NH_2⟨⟩$COOH$

p-Aminobenzoic acid

$CONH_2$

Nicotinamide

Biotin

Aneurin (Thiamine)

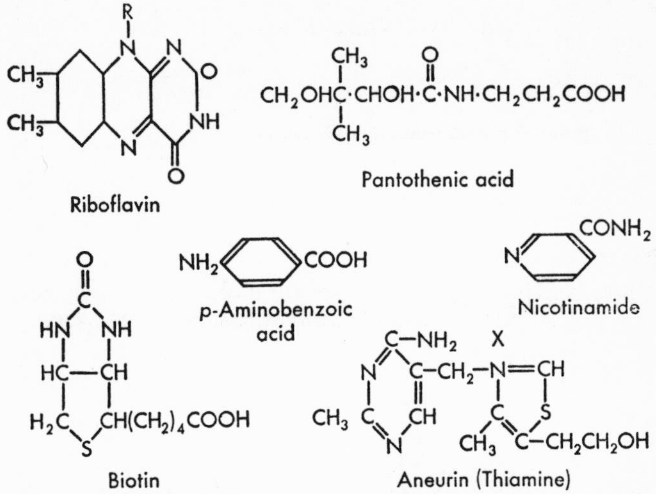

Figure 1. Some of the vitamins—substances essential to life.

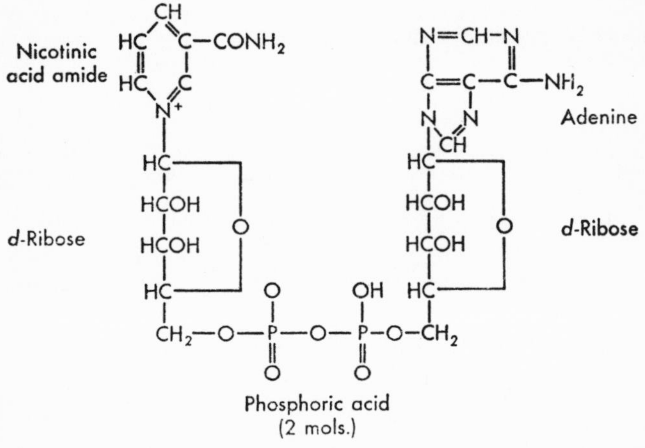

Nicotinic acid amide

Adenine

d-Ribose

d-Ribose

Phosphoric acid
(2 mols.)

Figure 2. Structual formula of co-enzyme I. ATP consists of the right-hand side (adenine and d-ribose) combined with three mols of phosphoric acid.

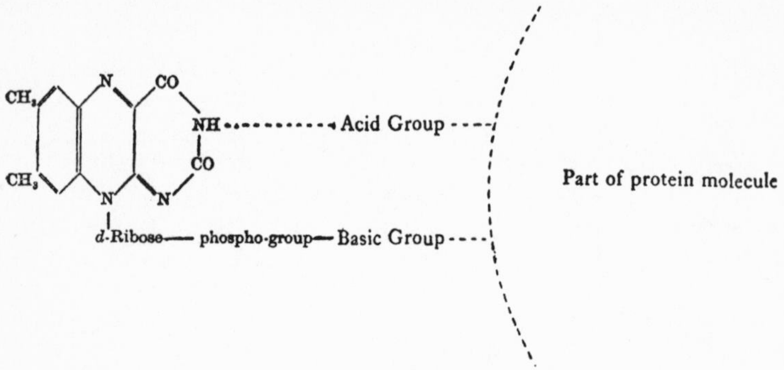

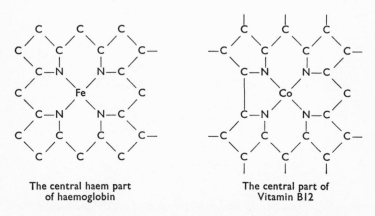

Figure 3. The riboflavin phosphate molecule showing how it combines with the protein part of the enzyme.

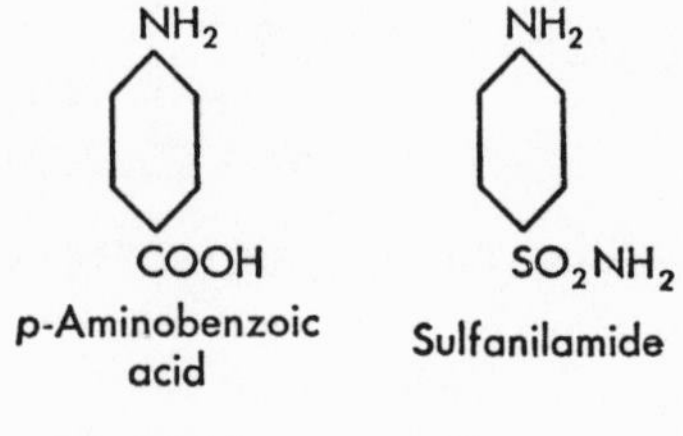

Figure 4. A vitamin and its antagonist.

Figure 5. The central parts of the molecules of haemoglobin and vitamin B_{12}.

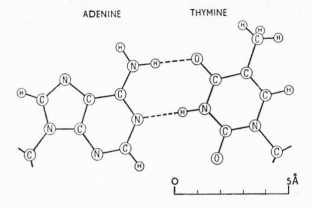

Figure 6. The bases present in nucleic acid (DNA) showing how they are bonded together by hydrogen bonds.

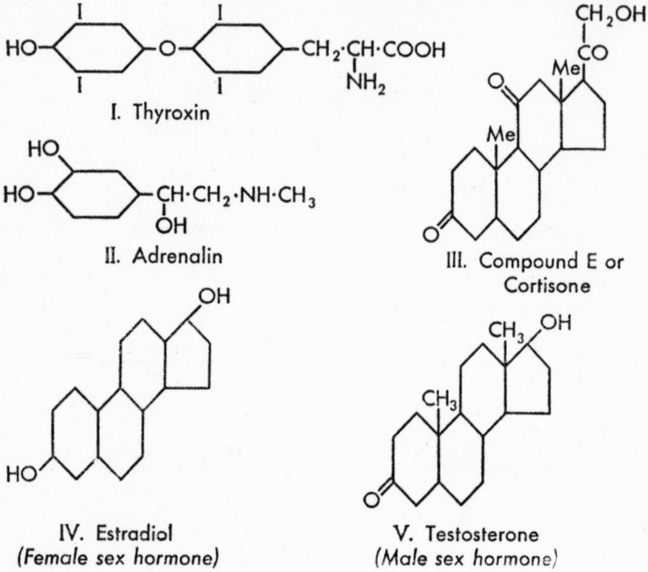

Figure 7. Some of the hormones.

Polycyclic hydrocarbons which occur in tars, such as benzpyrene. Certain dyestuffs, such as 'butter yellow', and other azo-dyes.

'Mustard gas' $S(CH_2.CH_2.Cl)_2$ and analogous compounds, such as nitrogen 'mustards', e.g., $CH_3N(CH_2.CH_2.Cl)_2$.

β-Naphthylamine and aminophenol, chemicals used in the dye-stuffs industry. The latter is formed naturally in the human bladder in some abnormal conditions and gives rise to bladder cancer.

Plastic films of various materials, embedded under the skin. Ionizing radiations from X-ray sets or from radioactive substances.

Fig. 8. Some carcinogenic agents.

Selected References and
Books for Further Reading

CHAPTERS I—III

Further information will be found in modern text books of biochemistry.

PROTEINS AND ENZYMES

Northrop, J. H., Kunitz, M. and Herriott, R. M., *Crystalline Enzymes* (Columbia Univ. Press, 2nd Edition, 1946).

Springall, H. D., *The Structural Chemistry of Proteins* (Butterworth, 1954).

Dixon, M. and Webb, E.C., *Enzymes* (Longmans Green, 1958).

Neurath, H. and Bailey, K., *The Proteins* (Acad. Press Inc., New York, 1954). (The standard work on proteins.)

Kendrew J. C. and others, *Nature*, **181**, 662, 1958.

CHAPTERS IV—V

For a good summary of recent work, see:

Crick, F. H. C., *Mechanisms of Biological Replication* (S.E.B. Symposia, Vol. XII, Cambridge Univ. Press, 1958).

Other references:

Watson, J. D. and Crick, F. H. C., *Nature*, **171**, 737, 1953.

Crick, F. H. C., Griffith, J. S. and Orgel, L. E., *Proc. Nat. Acad. Sciences* (U.S.A.), **43**, 416, 1957.

McElroy, W. D. and Glass, B. (ed.), *A Symposium on the Chemical Basis of Heredity* (Johns Hopkins Press, Baltimore, 1957).

Brachet, J., *Biochemical Cytology* (Acad. Press Inc., New York, 1957).

Engstrom, A. and Finean, J. B., *Biological Ultrastructure* (Acad. Press, New York, 1957).

Loftfield, R. B., *The biosynthesis of protein* in *Progress in Biophysics and Biophysical Chemistry*, Vol. 8 (Pergamon Press, London, 1957).

Palade, G. E., *J. Biochem. Biophys. Cytol.*, **2**, No. 4, suppl., 85 (1956) (concerning structures in cell cytoplasm).

Davidson, J. N., *The Biochemistry of the Nucleic Acids* (Methuen's Monographs on Biochemical Subjects, 2nd edition, 1953).

Taylor, J. H., Woods P. S., and Hughes W. L., *Proc. Nat. Acad. Sciences* (U.S.A.), **43**, 122, 1957.

CHAPTER VI

Griffith, F., *J. Hygiene* (Lond.), **27**, 113 (1928).

Dawson, M. H. and Sia, R. H. P., *J. exp. Med.*, **54**, 681 (1931).

Allaway, J. L., *ibid.*, **55**, 91 (1932).

Avery, O. T., MacLeod, C. M. and McCarty, M., *ibid.*, **79**, 137 (1944).

Benoit, J., Leroy, P., Vendrely, C. and Vendrely, R., *C. R. Acad. Sci.* (Paris), **244**, 2320 (1957); **245**, 448 (1957).

Hotchkiss, R. D., *Cold Spring Harbor Symp. Quant. Biol.*, **16**, 457 (1951).

Haldane, J. B. S., *The Biochemistry of Genetics* (Allen and Unwin, London, 1954).

Swanson, G. P., *Cytology and Cytogenetics* (Prentice-Hall, 1957).

CHAPTER VII

The Hazards to Man of Nuclear and Allied Radiations (Medical Research Council) H.M.S.O., London (1956).

Report of the Committee on Pathological Effects of Atomic Radiation (Nat. Acad. Sciences—N.R.C., Washington, 1956).

Bacq, Z. M. and Alexander, P., *Fundamentals of Radiobiology* (Butterworth, 1955).

Radiation Biology (ed. by A. Hollaender for National Research Council) (McGraw-Hill, 1954.)

CHAPTER VIII

Fraser, D., *et. al.*, *Proc. Nat. Acad. Sci.*, **43**, 939 (1957).

Fraenkel-Conrat, H. L., *J. Amer. Chem. Soc.*, **78**, 1882 (1957); *idem.*, *Biochim. Biophys. Acta*, **24**, 540 (1957); *idem.*, *Proc. Nat. Acad. Sci.*, **41**, 690 (1955).

Gierer, A. and Schramm, G., *Nature*, **177**, 702 (1956); *Z. Naturforsch.*, **11B**, 138 (1956).

Bawden, F. C., *Plant Viruses and Virus Diseases* (Chronica Botanica Co., 1956).

Jacob F. and Wollman E. L., in *A Symposium on the Chemical Basis of Heredity*, ed. W. D. McElroy and B. Glass (Johns Hopkins Press, Baltimore, 1957).

Stanley, W. M., *Science*, **81**, 644 (1935).

Hershey, A. D. and Chase, M., *J. Gen. Physiol.*, **36**, 39 (1952).

Benzer, S., *Proc. Nat. Acad. Sci.*, **41**, 344 (1955).

CHAPTERS IX—X

Raven, C. P., *Outline of Developmental Physiology* (Pergamon Press, 1954).

Waddington, C. H., *The Strategy of the Genes* (Allen and Unwin, 1957).

Brachet, J., *Chemical Embryology* (Interscience, New York, 1950).

Booth, L. G. and L. J., *Energetics of Development* (Columbia Univ. Press, 1954).

CHAPTER XI

Medawar, P. B., *The Uniqueness of the Individual* (Methuen, London, 1957).

Burnet, Sir F. Macfarlane, *Enzyme, Antigen and Virus* (Cambridge Univ. Press, 1956).

Boyd, W., *Fundamentals of Immunology* (Interscience, New York, 1956).

CHAPTER XII

Hieger, I., *One in Six* (Wingate, 1955).

Huxley, Sir Julian, *Biological Aspects of Cancer* (Allen and Unwin, 1958).

CHAPTER XIII

Bernal, J. D., *The Physical Basis of Life* (Routledge, 1951).

Oparin, A. I., *The Origin of Life on the Earth*, 3rd ed. (Oliver and Boyd, 1957).

Terrien, J., Truffaut, G. and Carles, J. *Light, Vegetation and Chlorophyll* (Hutchinson, 1957).

Hill, R. and Whittingham, C. P., *Photosynthesis* (Methuen's Biochemical Monographs, 1955).

CHAPTER XIV

MUSCLE THEORIES:

See Huxley, A. F., *Muscle Structure and Theories of Contraction*. In 'Progress in Biophysics and Biophysical Chemistry', Vol. VII (Pergamon Press, 1957).

Huxley, A. F. and Niedergerke, R., *Nature*, **173,** 971 (1954).

Huxley, H. E. and Hanson, J., *Nature*, **173,** 973 (1954).

VISION:

Pirenne, M. H., *Vision and the Eye* (Pilot Press, 1948).

Pieron, H., *The Sensations: their function, processes and mechanism* (trans. M. H. Pirenne and B. C. Abbott) (Muller, 1952).

NERVES:

Eccles, J. C., *The Neurophysiological Basis of Mind* (Oxford, 1953).

Fernandez-Moran, H., *The Submicroscopic Structure of Nerve Fibres*. In 'Progress in Biophysics and Biophysical Chemistry', Vol. IV, p. 122 (Pergamon Press, 1954).

CHAPTER XV

Sholl, D. A., *The Cerebral Cortex* (Methuen, 1957).

Adrian, E. D. (Lord Adrian), *Physical Background of Perception* (Oxford Univ. Press, 1947).

Sherrington, Sir C., *Man on his Nature* (Cambridge Univ. Press, 1957).

CHAPTER XVI

Craik, K. J. W., *The Nature of Explanation* (Cambridge Univ. Press, 1943).

Tinbergen, N., *The Study of Instinct* (Oxford Univ. Press, 1951).

Bierens de Haan, J. A., *Animal Psychology* (Hutchinson, 1949).

Physiological Mechanisms in Animal Behaviour. (Symposia of the Society for Experimental Biology, No. 4; Cambridge Univ. Press, 1950).

Schiller, H. (*ed.*), *Instinctive Behaviour* (Int. Univ. Press, New York, 1957). (A collection of the classic papers.)

CHAPTER XVIII

Hebb, D. O., *The Organisation of Behaviour* (John Wiley, 1949).

Sluckin, W., *Minds and Machines* (Pelican Books, 1954).

Wiener, N., *Cybernetics* (Wiley, 1948).

Walter, W. Grey, *The Living Brain* (Duckworth, 1953).

Ashley, W. R., *Design for a Brain* (Chapman and Hall, 1952).

von Neumann, J., *The Computer and the Brain* (Yale Univ. Press, 1957).

Lashley, K. S., *In Search of the Engram*. In 'Physiological Mechanisms of Animal Behaviour (Cambridge Univ. Press, 1950).

CHAPTER XIX

Medawar, P. B., *The Uniqueness of the Individual* (Methuen, London, 1957).

Comfort, A., *The Biology of Senescence* (Routledge and Kegan Paul, 1956).

Kapp, W. B. and Bourne, G. H., *The Biology of Ageing* (Symposia of Institute of Biology, No. 6, London, 1957).

INDEX

ACTH, 84
Adaptation, 97
Ageing, 150
Allergy, 89
Amino acids, 17
Amino acids, activation of, 51
Anaemia, sickle cell, 66
Aneurin, 30
Antibiotics, 34
Antibodies, 86
Antigens, 87
Antivitamins, 33
Atomic radiation, effects of, 58
Arrhenius, S., 102
ATP, 46
Auerbach, C., 64
Aureomycin, 34
Auxins, 78
Axons, 118

Bacterial flagellae, 111
Bacteriophage, 70
Beadle, G. N., 64
Benoit, J., 55
Benzer, S., 73
Bergson, H., 160
Biotin, 30, 65
Bladder cancer, 94
Blood groups, 89
Brain activity, 125
Brains, mechanical, 142
Brain, oscillations in, 125
Brown, Sir G. L., 114
Burnet, Sir F. M., 92

Calculating machines, 142
Calvin, M., 107
Cancer, 93
Cancer of bone, effect of radiations, 60
Carcinogenic agents, 64
Carcinogenic hydrocarbons, 94
Cerebral cortex, 144

Chain, E. B., 34
Chlorocruorin, 35
Chlorophyll, 35, 106
Chloromycetin, 34
Chloroplasts, 106
Cholesterol, 99
Chromosomes, 38
Chromosome breaks, 62
Chimera, 92
Citric Acid cycle, 46
Claude, A., 48
Cobalt deficiency, 37
Co-enzymes, 30
Collective mind, 158
Cook, J. W., 94
Consciousness, 147
Copper, effect of plant growth, 36
Cori, C. F., and G., 85
Cortisone, 83
Crick, F. H. C., 42, 51
Craik, K. J. N., 132
Cytoplasm, 48

Dale, Sir Henry, 114
Death, 150
Delbrück, M., 72
Descartes, R., 117
Diabetes, 21, 81
Differentiation, 76
DNA, 42
Ducks, transformation of, 55
Dodds, Sir Charles, 84

Endocrine glands, 84
Energy sources, 46
Entropy, 105
Enzymes, and genes, 66
Enzymes, 23
Elford, W. J., 67
Evolution, 155
Evolution of man, 137
Eye, 115

Feedback, 122
Fertilization, 40
Fildes, Sir P., 33
Fleming, Sir Ambrose, 33
Florey, Sir Howard, 34
Folic acid, 33
Fraenkel-Conrat, H. L., 71
Freewill, 135
Fungi, 33, 65

Galvani, L., 117
Genes, 38, 54
Genes and enzymes, 66
Germ cells, 39
Ghiberellic acid, 78
Gibbs, Willard, 105
Goitre, 81
Globulins, 88
Growth hormones, 78

Haddow, A., 95
Hayes, R. J. K., 137
Haemoglobin, 35
Haemolytic disease, 90
Hebb, D. O., 146
Hench, P. S., 83
Hieger, I., 94
Hill, R., 107
Hinshelwood, Sir C., 97
Hiroshima, 61
Histamine, 89
Haworth, Sir N., 29
Hodgkin, A. L., 119
Hofmeister, 18
Hopkins, Sir F. G., 28
Hormones, 80
Hormones, in cancer, 98
Huxley, A. F., 112, 119
Huxley, H. E., 112
Hydrocarbons, carcinogenic, 94
Hydrocarbons, natural, 103

Immunity, 86
Ingram, V. M., 66
Instinct, 131
Insulin, 19, 82, 85
Ionizations, 58

Jenner, Edward, 86

Kay, H. D., 110
Kelvin, Lord, 105
Kendall, E. S., 83
Kendrew, J. C., 21
Kennaway, Sir E., 94
Kögl, F., 78
Krebs cycle, 46
Krebs, Sir H. A., 46
Kunitz, M., 24

Lactation, 110
Lajtha, L. G., 45
Landsteiner, 88
Language, 139
Lashley, K. S., 145
Lethal does of radiation, 59
Learning, 123, 133
Leukemia, caused by atomic bombs, 61
Letré, H., 46
Lewis, J. N., 105
Li, C.-H., 84
Lippman, F., 51
Life span, effect of radiations, 60
Life span, 152
Longevity, 153
Lurea, S. E., 73

McIlwain, H., 31
Man, origin of, 137
Mayneord, W. V., 94
Medawar, P. B., 92
Memory, 127, 148
Memory, basis, 146
Metabolism of cell, 46
Metals, 35
Metamorphosis, 79
Micro-organisms, food requirements, 31
Micro-organisms, mutations of, 64
Micro-organisms, nutritional requirements, 65
Microsomes, 49
Milk formation, 110
Millott, N., 123

Mitochondria, 48
Models of outside world, 132
Molds, 31, 64
Morton, R. A., 116
Müller, H. T., 61
Muscle, 111
Mutation rate, effect of radiations on, 62
Mutations, 54, 61
Mutations, produced by X-rays, 58
Mutations of micro-organisms, 64
Mutations, produced by chemicals, 63
Mutation theory of cancer, 93
Myelin sheath, 118
Myoglobin, 21
Myosin, 112

Nerve impulse, 119
Nervous circle, 122
Nerves, 117
Neurones, 143
Neurospara, 64
Newton, Sir Isaac, 117
Niedergerke, R., 112
Northrop, J. H., 24, 104
Nucleic acids, 42
Nucleus, 38
Nucleolus, 49
Oestrogens, 83
Oestrogens, in cancer, 98
Oparin, A. I., 102
Optical activity, 104
Organizing factors, 77
Origin of life, 102

PAB, 33
Pancreas, 81
PAS, 33
Pavlov, I. P., 124
Pellagra, 29
Penfield, Sir W., 148
Penicillin, 33
Peptide chains, 17
Photosynthesis, 106
Photosynthesis, efficiency of, 108
Pituitary gland, 84

Pirenne, M. H., 115
Pneumococcus, transformation of, 54
Proteins, 16
Protein synthesis, 50

Radicals, 59
Reduction process, 39
Reflex action, 123
Reflex, conditioned, 124
Replication of DNA, 44
Respiratory proteins, 35
Retina, 115
Rhesus factor, 90
Rhodopsin, 116
Riboflavin, 30
Rickets, 29
Roentgen, W. K., 95
Roentgen (unit), 58
RNA, 50
RNA, of virus, 71
Rous, Peyton, 96
Russell, W. L., 61

Salivary gland chromosomes, 56
Sanger, F., 19
Schramm, G., 71
Sensations, 148
Sense organs, 114
Sex hormones, 83
Shaw, G. B., 153
Sheep disease, 36
Shope virus, 96
Skin grafts, 90
Smith, Lester, 37
Solar radiation, 108
Stanley, W. M., 67
Streptomycin, 34
Strontium, radioactive, in bone, 60
Sulphanilamides, 33
Sumner, J. B., 24
Superorganisms, 158
Suprarenals, 82
Svedberg, The, 18
Symbols, 140
Synapse, 143
Szent-Györgyi, A., 29, 112

Template code, 51
Thyroid gland, 80
Thyroxin, 81, 84
Tinbergen, N., 131
Tolerance, 92
Tools, 138
Transforming factors, 54

Vaccines, 87
Virus, 67
Virus particles, 19, 68
Virus, sizes of 19
Virus theory of cancer, 96
Vitamins, 28
Vitamin A, in vision, 116

Vitamin B12, 37

Warburg, O. H., 97
Wald, G., 116
Watson, J. B., 24
Watson, J. D., 42
Weiss, P., 77
Wigglesworth, V. B., 78
Wyckoff, R. W. G., 70

Xanthine oxidase, 37
X-rays, carcinogenicity of, 61
X-rays, effects of, 58

Young, J. Z., 124